How Chemical Reactions Occur

An Introduction to Chemical Kinetics
and Reaction Mechanisms

Edward L. King

University of Colorado

1964

W. A. BENJAMIN, INC.   New York   Amsterdam

HOW CHEMICAL REACTIONS OCCUR
An Introduction to Chemical Kinetics
and Reaction Mechanisms

Copyright © 1964 by W. A. Benjamin, Inc.

Library of Congress Catalog Card Number 63–8158
Manufactured in the United States of America
    at Kingsport Press, Inc., Kingsport, Tennessee

The manuscript was put into production on September 18, 1962,
    and this volume was published on April 30, 1963; second printing, with
    corrections, February 18, 1964

The publisher is pleased to acknowledge the assistance
    of Galen H. Fleck, who edited the manuscript,
    and William Prokos, who produced the illustrations

W. A. BENJAMIN, INC.,
2465 Broadway, New York 25, New York

Editor's Foreword

The teaching of general chemistry to beginning students becomes each day a more challenging and rewarding task as subject matter becomes more diverse and more complex and as the high school preparation of the student improves. These challenges have evoked a number of responses; this series of monographs for general chemistry is one such response. It is an experiment in the teaching of chemistry which recognizes a number of the problems that plague those who select textbooks and teach chemistry. First, it recognizes that no single book can physically encompass all the various aspects of chemistry that all instructors collectively deem important. Second, it recognizes that no single author is capable of writing authoritatively on all the topics that are included in everybody's list of what constitutes general chemistry. Finally, it recognizes the instructor's right to choose those topics that he considers to be important without having to apologize for having omitted large parts of an extensive textbook.

This volume, then, is one of approximately fifteen in the General Chemistry Monograph Series, each written by one or more highly qualified persons very familiar with the current status of the subject by virtue of research in it and also conversant with the problems associated with teaching the subject matter to beginning students. Each volume deals broadly with one of the subdivisions of general chemistry and constitutes a complete entity, far more comprehensive in its coverage than is permitted by the limitation of the standard one-volume text. Taken together, these volumes provide a range of topics from which the individual instructor can easily select those that will provide for his class an appropriate coverage of the material he considers most important.

Furthermore, inclusion of a number of topics that have only recently been considered for general chemistry courses, such as thermodynamics, molecular spectroscopy, and biochemistry, is planned, and these volumes will soon be available. In every instance a modern structural point of view has been adopted with the emphasis on general principles and unifying theory.

These volumes will have other uses also: selected monographs can be used to enrich the more conventional course of study by providing readily available, inexpensive supplements to standard texts. They should also prove valuable to students in other areas of the physical and biological sciences needing supplementary information in any field of chemistry pertinent to their own special interests. Thus, students of biology will find the monographs on biochemistry, organic chemistry, and reaction kinetics particularly useful. Beginning students in physics and meteorology will find the monograph on thermodynamics rewarding. Teachers of elementary science will also find these volumes invaluable aids to bringing them up to date in the various branches of chemistry.

Each monograph has several features which make it especially useful as an aid to teaching. These include a large number of solved examples and problems for the student, a glossary of technical terms, and copious illustrations.

The authors of the several monographs deserve much credit for their enthusiasm which made this experiment possible. Professor Rolfe Herber of Rutgers University has been of invaluable assistance in the preparation of this series, having supplied editorial comment and numerous valuable suggestions on each volume. Thanks are also due to Professor M. Kasha of the Florida State University for many suggestions during the planning stages and for reading several of the manuscripts.

RUSSELL JOHNSEN

Tallahassee, Florida
October 1962

Preface

This book provides an introduction to the dynamic aspects of chemical change—the rates of chemical reactions and the pathways by which they occur. These dynamic aspects are fundamental facets of chemistry. Knowledge of how chemical reactions occur is important from both theoretical and practical points of view. The effectiveness of a chemical process in industry may depend upon the rate of a particular reaction: an increase in rate by a factor of 10 can change red ink to black ink.

The material in this book is meant to be part of a first course in college chemistry. Beginning students should obtain a fairly sophisticated background in chemical kinetics and the meaning of rate laws in terms of reaction mechanisms so they can use these principles to understand the chemistry of both inorganic and organic substances. Because it is a basic part of chemistry, an introduction to chemical reactivity is important for the first-year student who will pursue the study of chemistry no further. To the first-year science major, the subject is crucial; and certainly to defer its instruction until a junior- or senior-level course in physical chemistry is to defer it too long.

I have attempted to present those theoretical and experimental aspects of the subject that can be understood by the intelligent student with a background of high school chemistry plus part of what is customarily covered in first-year college chemistry. The simplest ideas about the calculus notation are introduced, but it is not assumed that students using this book will have had calculus. It is more important for the beginning student to understand the meaning of a rate law than to be able to integrate rate laws of a variety of forms.   This is as true for the terminal student as it is for the chemistry major.

It is hoped that this book will also be a useful introduction, or reintroduction, to the subject for those at more advanced levels in related fields.

EDWARD L. KING

Boulder, Colorado
February 1, 1963

Contents

Contents   xi

I

Introduction

Some chemical reactions occur very rapidly and others occur very slowly. Most chemical reactions occur more rapidly the higher the temperature. One objective of this book is to explain these observations. Chemical kinetics is the part of chemical science dealing with the velocity of chemical reactions. The subject includes both the experimental study of reaction velocity and the development of theories to explain experimental results and to predict the outcome of experiments which have not yet been performed. Recent advances in experimental techniques have opened whole new areas of study. This is particularly true in the field of very fast reactions; measurement of the velocity of a reaction which occurs in one-thousandth of a second or even less is now possible. One experimental setup for studying fast reactions is shown in Fig. 1–1. Also, the theories of chemical kinetics continue to be improved, in some instances as the result of new high-speed computers making calculations which were once practically impossible.

Chemical kinetics has relevance in space technology. Chemical reactions of components of the air occur at the high temperatures realized when a space capsule reenters the atmosphere, Fig. 1–2. The rates of these endothermic reactions are pertinent in the dissipation of heat generated upon reentry. And, of course, before the problems of reentry are faced, the space vehicle has to get off the

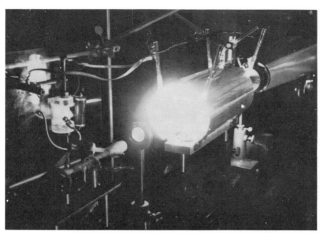

Figure 1–1. Flash photolysis. The upper photograph
shows the intense flash of light which causes a photochemical reaction to occur in the reaction cell. The
lower photograph shows the monitoring flash of light
which is set off a short time interval later. Light from
this flash goes through the reaction cell to the spectro-
graph at the upper right. Short-lived species formed in
the reaction cell by the intense flash of light are detected
by their characteristic spectra. The subject of flash
photolysis is discussed in Chapter 9. (These photographs
appeared in *Scientific American,* May, 1960, and are
reproduced with permission of the publisher.)

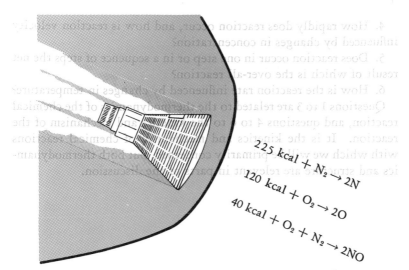

Figure 1-2. Endothermic chemical reactions which occur in the atmosphere at the high temperatures generated during reentry of a space capsule.

ground. This involves the kinetics of the exothermic chemical reactions that provide thrust to the rocket.

In an introduction to discussion of the rates of chemical reactions, the fundamental questions which can be posed should be reviewed. The composition of reactants and products must be known before a reaction can be considered characterized in even the simplest manner. The molecular structure of reactants and products should also be established; this is a problem of a varying degree of difficulty. In addition to asking for information regarding the composition and structure of reactants and products in a reaction, one may pose the questions:

1. To what extent does reaction go before chemical equilibrium is reached?

2. What heat effect accompanies chemical reaction?

3. How is the position of equilibrium influenced by changes in temperature?

4. How rapidly does reaction occur, and how is reaction velocity influenced by changes in concentration?

5. Does reaction occur in one step or in a sequence of steps the net result of which is the over-all reaction?

6. How is the reaction rate influenced by changes in temperature?

Questions 1 to 3 are related to the thermodynamics of the chemical reaction, and questions 4 to 6 to the kinetics and mechanism of the reaction. It is the kinetics and mechanism of chemical reactions with which we will be primarily concerned, but both thermodynamics and structure are relevant in parts of the discussion.

II

The Concept of Reaction Mechanism

C hemical reactions involve the forming and breaking of chemical bonds. The geometrical relationships of the atoms in the products are different from those in the reactants. A mixture of gaseous hydrogen and iodine is a simple example. In this mixture, pairs of hydrogen atoms are bonded together and pairs of iodine atoms are bonded together. Chemical reaction in this system produces hydrogen iodide,[1]

$$H_2 + I_2 = 2HI,$$

and after reaction the system contains molecules of hydrogen iodide in which an atom of hydrogen is bonded to an atom of iodine. Examination of the system before reaction and after reaction (Fig. 2-1) does not disclose the pathway by which the transformation occurs. The same point can be made with reference to the chemical equation for the change. A balanced equation for a net chemical change indicates only what species are consumed and what species are produced.

---

[1] An equality sign is used in a chemical equation if only the stoichiometry of the reaction is given by the equation.

5

How does atomic arrangement change from

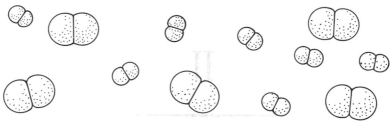

initial state

to

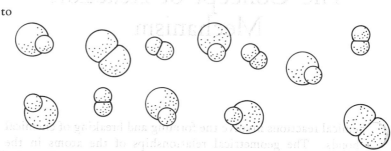

final state?

Figure 2–1. The initial and final states in a mixture of hydrogen and iodine which reacts to produce hydrogen iodide.

Such a chemical equation does not reveal the pathway by which reaction occurs, *nor is it intended to.*

The *reaction pathway*, also called the *reaction mechanism*, may be clarified by appropriate experimental investigation. The dependence of reaction rate upon the temperature and upon concentrations of reactants, products, and catalysts provides information about reaction mechanism. Experiments involving radioactive tracers may also contribute to understanding of reaction mechanisms.

A chemical reaction may occur in a single step, called an *elementary reaction*, or in a sequence of steps. The principal pathway for reac-

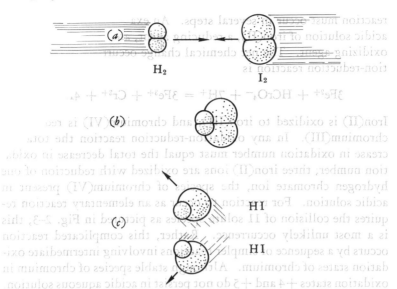

**Figure 2-2. The reaction of hydrogen and iodine,
$H_2 + I_2 = 2HI$. (a) Reactant molecules approach one
another. (b) Molecules collide with appropriate energy
and orientation. (c) Product molecules move away from
one another.**

tion of hydrogen and iodine to give hydrogen iodide the elementary reaction:[1]

$$H_2 + I_2 \rightleftarrows 2HI,$$

as pictured in Fig. 2-2. The concentration dependences of the reaction rate establish this as the reaction mechanism. This elementary reaction is relatively simple; it involves the breaking of two covalent bonds and the making of two covalent bonds. Elementary reactions are usually simple. Complicated chemical changes occur in a sequence of simple elementary reactions.

In some cases, complexity of the net chemical change suggests that

[1] The double arrow $\rightleftarrows$ is used in a chemical equation for a reversible elementary reaction.

reaction must occur in several steps. An example is the reaction in acidic solution of iron(II), a reducing agent, and chromium(VI), an oxidizing agent. The net chemical change occurring in this oxidation-reduction reaction is

$$3Fe^{2+} + HCrO_4^- + 7H^+ = 3Fe^{3+} + Cr^{3+} + 4H_2O.$$

Iron(II) is oxidized to iron(III), and chromium(VI) is reduced to chromium(III). In any oxidation-reduction reaction the total increase in oxidation number must equal the total decrease in oxidation number; three iron(II) ions are oxidized with reduction of one hydrogen chromate ion, the species of chromium(VI) present in acidic solution. For reaction to occur as an elementary reaction requires the collision of 11 solute species as pictured in Fig. 2–3; this is a most unlikely occurrence. Rather, this complicated reaction occurs by a sequence of simpler reactions involving intermediate oxidation states of chromium. Although stable species of chromium in oxidation states $+4$ and $+5$ do not persist in acidic aqueous solution, they may have a transitory existence during reactions in which chromium(VI) is converted to chromium(III), as in the reaction under consideration. Oxidation of one iron(II) ion to iron(III) by hydrogen chromate ion would produce a species of unstable chromium(V); oxidation of one iron(II) ion to iron(III) by chromium(V) would produce a species of unstable chromium(IV); and oxidation of one iron(II) ion by chromium(IV) would produce chromium(III), the stable end product of reduction of chromium(VI). Although a sequence of three successive reactions in each of which one equivalent of oxidation and one equivalent of reduction occur is a reasonable mechanism for this reaction of chromium(VI), a three-equivalent oxidizing agent, and iron(II), a one-equivalent reducing agent, only appropriate experimental evidence sheds light upon whether this *is* the reaction mechanism. Studies of the rate of this reaction give support to the mechanism pictured in Fig. 2–4.

Steps involved in the chromium(VI)-chromium(III) transformation can also be probed by using the relatively powerful one-equivalent oxidizing agent, cerium(IV). Studies of the rate of oxidation of chromium(III) to chromium(VI) by cerium(IV),

$$3Ce^{4+} + Cr^{3+} + 4H_2O = 3Ce^{3+} + HCrO_4^- + 7H^+,$$

also suggest participation of chromium(IV) and chromium(V) as unstable intermediates. The relevant experimental evidence will be considered later.

One should not, however, be misled to expect that a reaction proceeds by a simple mechanism just because the equation for the net reaction is simple. Even a reaction with simple stoichiometry may occur by a sequence of steps. An example is the gaseous reaction of hydrogen and bromine to give hydrogen bromide:

$$H_2 + Br_2 = 2HBr.$$

A collision of these

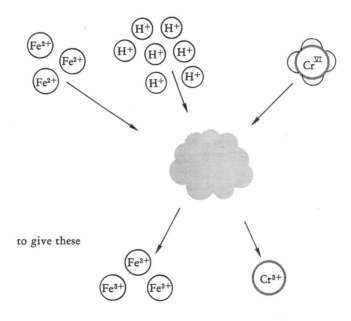

to give these

is very, very improbable.

Figure 2–3. An improbable mechanism for the reaction of chromium(VI) and iron(II). (Water molecules produced in reaction are not shown.)

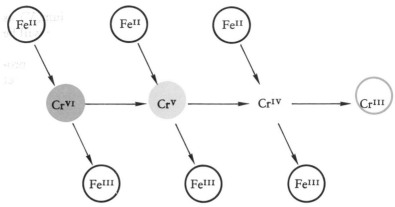

Figure 2–4. The stepwise reduction of chromium(VI). In each step, iron(II) is oxidized to iron(III) and the oxidation number of chromium decreases by one unit.

Kinetic studies have shown this reaction to occur by the mechanism

$$Br_2 \rightleftarrows 2Br$$
$$Br + H_2 \rightarrow HBr + H$$
$$H + Br_2 \rightarrow HBr + Br$$

with the sum of the last two reactions being the net reaction. The first reaction provides bromine atoms to initiate the sequence of two reactions which can repeat over and over again. This reaction mechanism is called a *chain mechanism*. Although the principal pathway for the hydrogen-iodine reaction is the single elementary reaction already discussed, a chain mechanism becomes increasingly important at elevated temperatures. The hydrogen-chlorine reaction has a feature not shared by the hydrogen-iodine and hydrogen-bromine reactions. Under certain experimental conditions, hydrogen-chlorine mixtures explode. This is caused by the large amount of heat evolved in the reaction

$$H_2 + Cl_2 = 2HCl.$$

As reaction occurs, the evolved heat raises the temperature and makes the reaction occur faster, which liberates still more heat, etc., etc., until *boom!*

One exciting area of modern chemistry is the investigation of reaction mechanisms. Chemists want to know how reactions occur. There is more to the study of reaction mechanisms than simply the challenge to the intellect. Understanding of reaction mechanisms may make it possible to select reaction conditions leading to a higher yield of desired products and a lower yield of undesired ones in important industrial processes.

PROBLEMS

1. The decomposition of nitrogen dioxide,

$$2NO_2 = 2NO + O_2,$$

occurs in a sequence of two elementary reactions at very high temperatures. The net change in the first of these is

$$NO_2 = NO + O.$$

What additional single reactions, when combined with this reaction, give the complete reaction? (There are two possibilities. In Chap. 5 you will learn more about this reaction, and on that basis you will be able to understand why one of these possibilities is the one the system employs.)

2. The net reaction that occurs when a strong base (e.g., sodium hydroxide) neutralizes acetic acid, a weak acid, is

$$HOAc + OH^- = OAc^- + H_2O.$$

In many elementary textbooks, it is suggested, with no real basis for the suggestion, that the mechanism for this reversible reaction is

$$HOAc + H_2O \rightleftarrows H_3O^+ + OAc^-$$
$$H_3O^+ + OH^- \rightleftarrows 2H_2O.$$

Suggest another possible mechanism for this net reaction. Since the over-all reaction occurs very rapidly, it is only by recently developed methods of studying the rates of very fast reactions (see Chap. 9) that the mechanism of this reaction can be discovered. Think about the way in which kinetic data would distinguish the two possible mechanisms.

III

Reaction Kinetics

Chemical reactions occur with a wide range of rates. Some occur almost instantaneously; others occur at so low a rate that for all practical purposes the reaction does not take place. The usefulness of a particular chemical reaction as a preparative procedure obviously depends upon its rate. For this reason, knowledge of factors which influence reaction velocity has practical consequences. In addition, as already stated, one kind of information which sheds light upon the mechanism of a chemical reaction is its velocity and the temperature and concentration dependences of the velocity. We shall consider these topics at some length, but first it is appropriate to consider the definition of reaction rate and ways it can be measured.

3–1. THE CONCEPT OF REACTION RATE

It is customary to express reaction rate as the change in concentration of a reactant or product per unit time. Expressed in this way, reaction rate does not depend upon the size of the sample under consideration. Although more product is produced in a particular time interval in 10 liters of reaction mixture than in 100 ml of the same mixture, the reaction rate is the same in the two samples.

If the concentration of a reactant A decreases from 0.100 mole/liter to 0.083 mole/liter in 10.6 min, the average rate of reaction during this interval can be calculated:

$$\text{average rate} = \frac{\text{change in concentration of A}}{\text{elapsed time}}$$

$$= \frac{(0.100 - 0.083) \text{ mole/liter}}{10.6 \text{ min}}$$

$$= 1.6 \times 10^{-3} \text{ mole/liter/min.}$$

The symbol Δ is used to represent change, and the above calculation can be formulated:[1]

$$\text{average rate} = -\frac{\Delta[A]}{\Delta t} = -\frac{[A]_2 - [A]_1}{t_2 - t_1}$$

$$= -\frac{(0.083 - 0.100) \text{ mole/liter}}{10.6 \text{ min}}$$

$$= 1.6 \times 10^{-3} \text{ mole/liter/min.}$$

The sign convention in the above equation is so chosen that the rate of reaction is a positive quantity even though the concentration of A is decreasing with increasing time.

Actual data from which reaction rates can be obtained will clarify the calculation of the preceding paragraph. We shall consider the decomposition of dinitrogen pentoxide dissolved in carbon tetrachloride. Dinitrogen pentoxide, the anhydride of nitric acid, decomposes to give nitrogen dioxide,[2] which is soluble in carbon tetrachloride, and oxygen, which is not:

$$2N_2O_5 = 4NO_2 + O_2(g).$$

This reaction occurs in various inert solvents and in the gas phase; in water, the reaction

$$N_2O_5 + H_2O = 2H^+ + 2NO_3^-$$

occurs instead. The oxygen produced is quite insoluble in carbon tetrachloride, and the extent of reaction can be followed by meas-

---

[1] A formula in brackets, for example [A], represents the concentration of the indicated species in moles per liter.

[2] Depending upon its concentration, nitrogen dioxide may be present in monomeric or dimeric form; the position of equilibrium in the reaction $2NO_2 \rightleftharpoons N_2O_4$ depends upon the concentration. (The special type of double arrow $\rightleftharpoons$ is used in chemical equations for equilibria which are rapidly established.)

uring the volume of oxygen evolved as a function of time. From these data and consideration of the balanced equation, the concentration of unreacted dinitrogen pentoxide can be calculated. Such values from an actual experiment are given in Table 3-1. The average rate at which the concentration of dinitrogen pentoxide decreases in the interval between successive readings at t_1 and t_2 is calculated:

$$\text{average rate} = -\frac{\Delta[N_2O_5]}{\Delta t} = -\frac{[N_2O_5]_2 - [N_2O_5]_1}{t_2 - t_1}.$$

Table 3-1

The Rate of Decomposition of Dinitrogen Pentoxide in Carbon Tetrachloride Solution[a]

$$2N_2O_5 = 4NO_2 + O_2(g)$$
$$T = 45°C$$

Time, min	Δt, min	$[N_2O_5]$, moles/liter	$\Delta[N_2O_5]$, moles/liter	$-\dfrac{\Delta[N_2O_5]}{\Delta t}$, moles/liter/min
0		2.33		
	184		0.25	1.36×10^{-3}
184		2.08		
	135		0.17	1.26×10^{-3}
319		1.91		
	207		0.24	1.16×10^{-3}
526		1.67		
	341		0.32	0.94×10^{-3}
867		1.35		
	331		0.24	0.72×10^{-3}
1198		1.11		
	679		0.39	0.57×10^{-3}
1877		0.72		

[a] Data from the work of H. Eyring and F. Daniels, *J. Am. Chem. Soc.*, **52**, 1472 (1930).

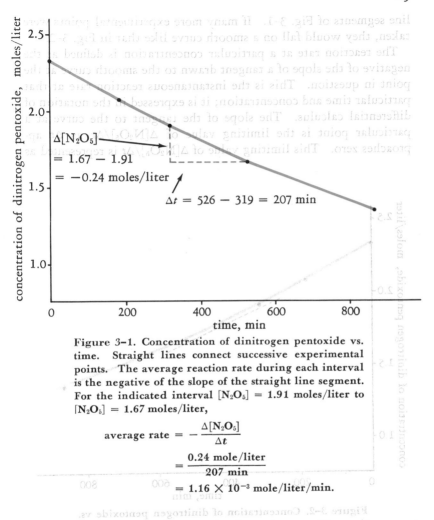

Figure 3–1. Concentration of dinitrogen pentoxide vs. time. Straight lines connect successive experimental points. The average reaction rate during each interval is the negative of the slope of the straight line segment. For the indicated interval [N₂O₅] = 1.91 moles/liter to [N₂O₅] = 1.67 moles/liter,

$$\text{average rate} = -\frac{\Delta[N_2O_5]}{\Delta t}$$

$$= \frac{0.24 \text{ mole/liter}}{207 \text{ min}}$$

$$= 1.16 \times 10^{-3} \text{ mole/liter/min.}$$

Data from Table 3–1 are plotted in Fig. 3–1, in which straight lines connect adjacent experimental points. The slope of each straight line segment is, by definition, the negative of the average value of the rate during the interval. The values of average rate decrease as reaction proceeds. The actual decrease in rate is gradual and continuous, and not discontinuous as implied by the connected straight line segments of Fig. 3–1. If many more experimental points were taken, they would fall on a smooth curve like that in Fig. 3–2.

The reaction rate at a particular concentration is defined as the negative of the slope of a tangent drawn to the smooth curve at the point in question. This is the instantaneous reaction rate at that particular time and concentration; it is expressed in the notation of differential calculus. The slope of the tangent to the curve at a particular point is the limiting value of $\Delta[N_2O_5]/\Delta t$ as Δt approaches zero. This limiting value of $\Delta[N_2O_5]/\Delta t$ is represented as

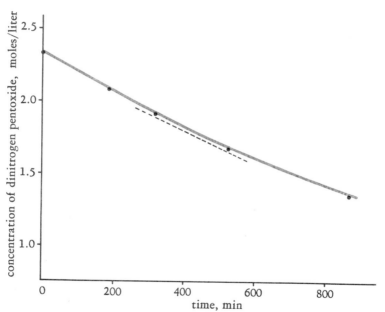

Figure 3–2. Concentration of dinitrogen pentoxide vs. time. The experimental points are the same as those shown in Fig. 3–1. The reaction rate at a particular concentration is the negative of the slope of a tangent drawn to the curve at that concentration, as indicated at $[N_2O_5] = 1.79$ moles/liter. At this point

$$-\frac{d[N_2O_5]}{dt} = 1.11 \times 10^{-3} \text{ mole/liter/min.}$$

$$\frac{d[\text{N}_2\text{O}_5]}{dt} = \lim_{\Delta t \to 0} \frac{\Delta[\text{N}_2\text{O}_5]}{\Delta t},$$

where $d[\text{N}_2\text{O}_5]/dt$ is the derivative of the dinitrogen pentoxide concentration with respect to time. The rate of reaction of dinitrogen pentoxide at a particular concentration is the negative of the derivative at that concentration:

$$\text{reaction rate} = -\frac{d[\text{N}_2\text{O}_5]}{dt}.$$

3-2. METHODS OF MEASURING REACTION VELOCITY

The extent of reaction as a function of time may be determined in a number of ways. Which of the available methods will prove practical depends on the nature of the reaction. Ideally one wants to measure the reaction rate without disturbing the course of the reaction. In the case of the decomposition of dinitrogen pentoxide in solution,

$$2\text{N}_2\text{O}_5 = 4\text{NO}_2 + \text{O}_2(g),$$

the volume of oxygen evolved as a function of time can be measured by using a gas buret as illustrated in Fig. 3-3.

If a reaction in solution is one in which the number and/or nature of the ionic species changes, the electrical conductance of the solution probably will change as reaction proceeds. If the reaction mixture is placed in a conductance cell, as shown in Fig. 3-4, a series of readings of the conductance of the solution as reaction proceeds provides data from which the rate of reaction can be calculated. The hydrolysis of an alkyl halide, a covalent substance, gives hydrogen ion and halide ion:

$$\underset{\textbf{alkyl halide}}{\text{RX}} + \text{H}_2\text{O} = \underset{\textbf{alcohol}}{\text{ROH}} + \text{H}^+ + \text{X}^-,$$

in which R represents a hydrocarbon radical, for example, C_2H_5, the ethyl radical, and X represents a halogen. This reaction is one that can be followed by measuring the conductance of the reaction mixture. The hydrolysis of an ester in alkaline solution, for instance

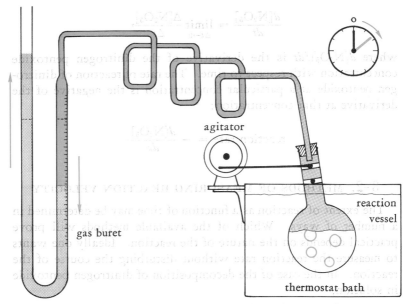

Figure 3–3. Gas buret for measuring the rate of a reaction in which gas is evolved. The flexible glass connection allows sufficient agitation to prevent supersaturation of the solution with gas.

tertiary butyl acetate to form tertiary butyl alcohol and acetate ion,

$$CH_3CO_2C(CH_3)_3 + OH^- = (CH_3)_3COH + CH_3CO_2^-,$$

can also be followed in this manner. Although in this example the number of ions is not altered as reaction proceeds, the acetate ion, which is a product, moves less rapidly in an electric field than the hydroxide ion, which is a reactant. Therefore, the conductance of the reaction mixture decreases with time as hydrolysis occurs.

Reactions involving colored species can be followed by measuring light absorption as a function of time. It is necessary to demonstrate that the light used in measurement does not influence the reaction

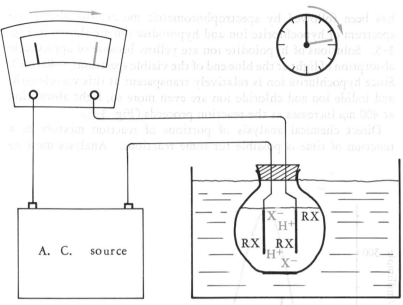

Figure 3–4. Measurement of conductance of a reaction mixture as a function of time. In the reaction

$$RX + H_2O = ROH + H^+ + X^-$$

hydrogen ion and halide ion are produced as reaction occurs. These ions move in the alternating electric field created by the oscillator, but the neutral molecule RX does not.

velocity. Light influences many chemical reactions, but light of relatively low intensity, and therefore slight influence, may be employed if light absorption is measured with a modern spectrophotometer.[1] The oxidation of iodide ion by hypochlorite ion in alkaline solution,

$$ClO^- + I^- = IO^- + Cl^-,$$

[1] A spectrophotometer measures the transmission of light by a sample. The wavelength of light may be varied. In some automatic recording instruments, the plot of light absorption at some particular wavelength as a function of time may be obtained directly.

has been followed by spectrophotometric means; the absorption spectrum of hypochlorite ion and hypoiodite ion are shown in Fig. 3–5. Solutions of hypoiodite ion are yellow because of appreciable absorption of light at the blue end of the visible spectrum ($\sim$400 mμ). Since hypochlorite ion is relatively transparent at this wavelength, and iodide ion and chloride ion are even more so, light absorption at 400 mμ increases as the reaction proceeds (Fig. 3–6).

Direct chemical analysis of portions of reaction mixture as a function of time is possible for some reactions. Analysis must be

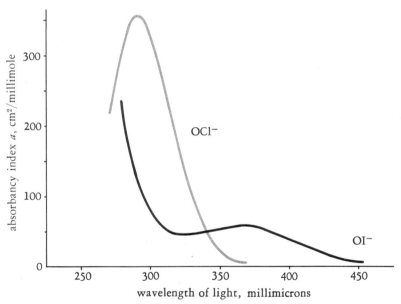

Figure 3–5. Absorption of light by hypoiodite ion and hypochlorite ion as a function of wavelength. The absorbancy index of a dissolved species is related to its light absorption:

$$a = \frac{\log \ (I_0/I)}{\text{concentration} \times \text{cell length}},$$

where I_0 and I are the intensities of light transmitted by the solvent and the solution, respectively. (One millimicron, 1 mμ, is equal to 10^{-7} cm.)

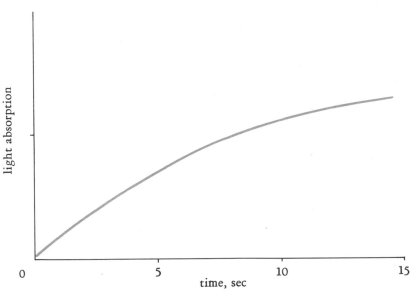

Figure 3–6. Light absorption at 400 mμ of a solution in which the reaction

$$OCl^- + I^- = OI^- + Cl^-$$

is occurring.

carried out in such a way that the reaction does not occur to an appreciable extent during the procedure. A reaction may be stopped effectively at a particular instant by appropriate alteration in the system. This is called quenching the reaction. Some quenching procedures are based on the fact that reaction rates generally decrease if the temperature is lowered. The rates of some reactions in solution can be decreased enormously by a tenfold dilution with chilled solvent. If the reaction rate is low enough and has a large enough temperature coefficient, it may be possible to quench the reaction simply by cooling the undiluted solution in an ice bath.

PROBLEMS

1. The concentration of a reactant A changes from 0.0350 *M* to 0.0285 *M* in 23 min. What is the average reaction rate during this time interval? Express your answer in two ways; use both the second and the minute as the unit of time.

(Ans.: 2.83 × 10⁻⁴ mole/liter/min or 4.7 × 10⁻⁶ mole/liter/sec)

2. The closer together the experimental points giving the concentration of A, the more nearly does $\Delta[A]/\Delta t$ approach $d[A]/dt$. Since it is the latter quantity which is really of more interest, you might expect that kineticists would choose to evaluate $\Delta[A]/\Delta t$ from closely spaced experimental points. They do not. What disadvantage in evaluating the average rate of change of concentration of A from experimental points which are close together can you suggest?

3. From the first two data points in Table 3–1, one calculates an average rate of disappearance of dinitrogen pentoxide of 1.36 × 10⁻³ mole/liter/min. What is the average rate of appearance of nitrogen dioxide (NO₂) in this same time interval?

4. If the gas buret shown in Fig. 3–3 is used to follow the decomposition of dinitrogen pentoxide with the gas being measured at a pressure of 750 mm of mercury and a temperature of 22°C, what volume of oxygen gas was given off in the first 184 min of the experiment described in Table 3–1. The volume of reaction solution was 40.0 ml.   *(Ans.: 123 ml)*

IV

Experimental Rate Laws

The rate of a chemical reaction at a given temperature depends upon the concentration of one or more of the reactants; it may also depend upon the concentrations of reaction product(s). An equation relating reaction rate $d[P]/dt$ and concentrations is called a rate law. The rate law for a reaction *must* be established by experimental measurement; it cannot be predicted from consideration of the balanced equation for the net reaction. One can, however, derive mathematically the rate law corresponding to a particular assumed mechanism. For different assumed mechanisms, the derived rate laws generally have different forms. This is not invariably the case; different mechanisms may have rate laws of the same form. Comparison of an experimentally observed rate law with derived rate laws then allows one to make some choice among plausible mechanisms. Only mechanisms yielding rate laws of the form found by experiment may be considered as possible mechanisms for the reaction.

Before discussing the experimental establishment of a rate law, let us examine one particular experimental rate law with the objective of introducing nomenclature. The rate of oxidation of bromide ion by bromate ion in acidic aqueous solution,

$$5Br^- + BrO_3^- + 6H^+ = 3Br_2 + 3H_2O,$$

23

is proportional to the first power of the concentration of bromide ion, the first power of the concentration of bromate ion, and the second power of the concentration of hydrogen ion; this can be expressed in the rate law

$$\frac{d[Br_2]}{dt} = k[Br^-][BrO_3^-][H^+]^2.$$

The derivative $d[Br_2]/dt$ expresses the rate of increase of bromine concentration in the reaction mixture containing bromide ion, bromate ion, and hydrogen ion at the specified concentrations. The proportionality constant k is called the *rate constant;* it has a particular numerical value at each temperature. The exponent of a concentration factor is the *reaction order* for that species. The above reaction is first order in bromide ion, first order in bromate ion, and second order in hydrogen ion. For a rate law of this type (a single term made up of one or more concentration factors) the sum of the exponents is the total reaction order. This is a fourth-order rate law. The reaction orders in this case are not identical to the coefficients in the balanced chemical equation. One cannot assume they will be; it is for this reason that the form of the rate law for a reaction must be determined experimentally.

QUESTION:

In the rate law

$$\frac{d[I_3^-]}{dt} = k[I^-][H_3AsO_4][H^+]$$

for the reaction

$$3I^- + H_3AsO_4 + 2H^+ = I_3^- + H_3AsO_3 + H_2O,$$

what is the reaction order with respect to iodide ion? What is the total reaction order?

Since a rate law expresses the dependence of reaction rate upon concentration, it is established by experimental determination of the reaction rate at different concentrations. The form of a rate law may be obtained from a single experiment during which concentrations of reactants (and products) change greatly. Or it may prove more informative to correlate the reaction rate observed in several experiments run at different initial concentrations.

4–1. A FIRST-ORDER RATE LAW

Let us first consider the rate of decomposition of dinitrogen pentoxide in carbon tetrachloride, values of which are given in Table 3–1. In a rigorous approach to this problem, values of reaction rate defined by the derivative

$$\text{reaction rate} = -\frac{d[N_2O_5]}{dt}$$

would be correlated with the concentration of dinitrogen pentoxide. The slopes of straight lines connecting the adjacent experimental points are, however, approximately equal to the slopes of tangents to the smooth curve at points midway between the experimental points in question. The average reaction rate decreases in each successive time interval. It is reasonable to attribute this to the lower concentration of dinitrogen pentoxide in each successive time interval. If the reaction rate were proportional to the first power of the concentration of dinitrogen pentoxide,

$$-\frac{d[N_2O_5]}{dt} \propto [N_2O_5],$$

the quotient

$$-\frac{1}{[N_2O_5]_{av}} \times \frac{\Delta[N_2O_5]}{\Delta t}$$

would have an approximately constant value. On the other hand, if the reaction rate were proportional to the second power of the concentration of dinitrogen pentoxide,

$$-\frac{d[N_2O_5]}{dt} \propto [N_2O_5]^2,$$

the quotient

$$-\frac{1}{[N_2O_5]_{av}^2} \times \frac{\Delta[N_2O_5]}{\Delta t}$$

would have an approximately constant value. If the reaction rate is known as a function of the reactant concentration, the quotient of reaction rate and various powers of reactant concentration can be calculated. The reaction order is established if one of these quotients has an approximately constant value.

In Table 4–1 the average reaction rate, $-\Delta[N_2O_5]/\Delta t$, is corre-lated with the average concentration of dinitrogen pentoxide. Over a 2.4-fold range of concentration of dinitrogen pentoxide, the quo-tient of average rate and first power of this concentration is essen-tially constant; what variation there is can be attributed to experi-mental error. The quotient of average rate and second power of the concentration of dinitrogen pentoxide is far from constant. If $(-\Delta[N_2O_5]/\Delta t)/[N_2O_5]_{av}$ is essentially constant over a 2.4-fold range in the value of $[N_2O_5]_{av}$, the values of $(-\Delta[N_2O_5]/\Delta t)/[N_2O_5]_{av}^2$ over this same range of concentration change by a factor of 2.4.

Direct proportionality between the rate of decomposition of dini-trogen pentoxide and its concentration is expressed in the first-order rate law

$$- \frac{d[N_2O_5]}{dt} = k[N_2O_5],$$

Table 4–1

A Correlation of Reaction Rate and Concentration of Dinitrogen Pentoxide[a]

$$2N_2O_5 = 4NO_2 + O_2(g)$$

$T = 45°$ Solvent: carbon tetrachloride

$[N_2O_5]_{av}$, moles/liter	$-\dfrac{\Delta[N_2O_5]}{\Delta t}$ = avg rate, moles/liter/min	$\dfrac{Avg\ rate}{[N_2O_5]_{av}}$, min^{-1}	$\dfrac{Avg\ rate}{[N_2O_5]_{av}^2}$, liters/mole/min
2.21	1.36×10^{-3}	6.2×10^{-4}	2.8×10^{-4}
2.00	1.26×10^{-3}	6.3×10^{-4}	3.2×10^{-4}
1.79	1.16×10^{-3}	6.5×10^{-4}	3.6×10^{-4}
1.51	0.94×10^{-3}	6.2×10^{-4}	4.1×10^{-4}
1.23	0.72×10^{-3}	5.9×10^{-4}	4.8×10^{-4}
0.92	0.57×10^{-3}	6.2×10^{-4}	6.7×10^{-4}

[a] Columns 1 and 2 are derived from Table 3–1.

in which the calculus notation is used. The quotient of reaction rate and the first power of the concentration of dinitrogen pentoxide is the rate constant

$$-\frac{1}{[N_2O_5]}\frac{d[N_2O_5]}{dt} = k.$$

Based on the correlation outlined in Table 4–1, the rate constant for this rate law is, therefore, the average of calculated values of $(-\Delta[N_2O_5]/\Delta t)/[N_2O_5]_{av}$, that is, 6.2×10^{-4} min^{-1}. At 45°C in carbon tetrachloride as solvent, the rate law for decomposition of dinitrogen pentoxide is

$$-\frac{d[N_2O_5]}{dt} = 6.2 \times 10^{-4}\,[N_2O_5]\ \text{mole/liter/min}.$$

With this rate law, the rate of decomposition of dinitrogen pentoxide in carbon tetrachloride at 45°C can be calculated for any concentration.

QUESTION:

What is the rate of decomposition of dinitrogen pentoxide in carbon tetrachloride at 45°C if the concentration is 0.40 mole/liter?
(*Ans.: 2.48 × 10⁻⁴ mole/liter/min*)

A rate law is a differential equation, that is, an equation involving a derivative. Differential equations of particular forms can be converted to equations not involving derivatives by the methods of integral calculus. The integrated form of the first-order rate law is

$$\frac{[N_2O_5]}{[N_2O_5]_0} = e^{-kt},$$

where $[N_2O_5]_0$ is the concentration of dinitrogen pentoxide at zero time and e is $2.71828 \ldots$, the base of natural logarithms. The value of e is the sum of the infinite series

$$e = 1 + \frac{1}{1!} + \frac{1}{2!} + \frac{1}{3!} + \frac{1}{4!} + \frac{1}{5!} + \cdots$$

$$= 1 + 1 + \frac{1}{2} + \frac{1}{6} + \frac{1}{24} + \frac{1}{120} + \cdots$$

The integrated rate equation is converted to

$$\ln [N_2O_5] - \ln [N_2O_5]_0 = -kt$$

by taking the logarithm of each side.   In terms of logarithms to the base 10, the equation becomes

$$\log [N_2O_5] - \log [N_2O_5]_0 = -\frac{k}{2.303}\, t,$$

since

$$\ln 10 = 2.303 \quad \text{and} \quad \ln [N_2O_5] = 2.303 \log [N_2O_5].$$

(Natural logarithms are designated ln or $\log_e$ and logarithms to

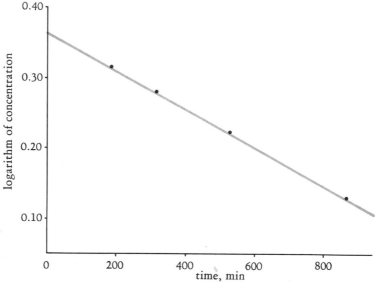

Figure 4–1. A plot of logarithm of dinitrogen pentoxide concentration vs. time.   The equation for the straight line is

$$\log [N_2O_5] = \log [N_2O_5]_0 - \frac{k}{2.303}\, t$$

(These are the same points that are plotted in Figs. 3–1 and 3–2.)   The value of k can be obtained from the slope of this straight line: $-k = 2.303 \times$ slope.

the base 10 are designated log.) Figure 4–1 shows the data of Table 3–1 plotted as log $[N_2O_5]$ vs. time. The linearity proves the reaction is first order.

Associated with a first-order rate law is the concept of half-time for reaction $t_{1/2}$. If $[N_2O_5] = \frac{1}{2}[N_2O_5]_0$, we have

$$\frac{[N_2O_5]}{[N_2O_5]_0} = \frac{1}{2} = e^{-kt_{1/2}}$$

The magnitudes of rate constant and half-time are related:

$$\frac{1}{2} = e^{-k\,t_{1/2}}.$$

By taking the logarithm of each side of the equation, we obtain

$$-\ln 2 = -kt_{1/2}$$

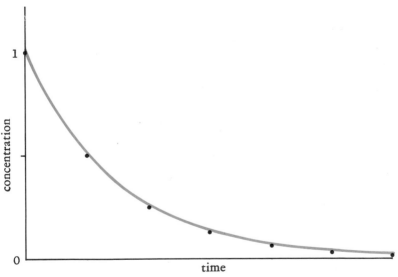

Figure 4–2. Concentration vs. time in a first-order reaction. Successive points are separated by one half-time.

and, therefore,

$$k = \frac{\ln 2}{t_{1/2}} = \frac{0.693}{t_{1/2}}.$$

For the reaction in question, the half-time obtained from Fig. 4–1 is 1110 min; the value of k that is derived from this half-time is 6.2×10^{-4} min^{-1}, which agrees with the value that is shown derived in Table 4–1.

During each successive half-time, one-half of the reactant which was present at the start of the period reacts. After two half-times, the amount of reactant remaining is $\frac{1}{2} \times \frac{1}{2} = \frac{1}{4}$ of the amount initially present. After three half-times, $\frac{1}{2} \times \frac{1}{2} \times \frac{1}{2} = \frac{1}{8}$ of the amount present initially remains. This is shown in Fig. 4–2.

Among the many natural processes conforming to a first-order rate law is the decay of a radioactive isotope. The rate of decay in a sample of N atoms is proportional to N:

$$-\frac{dN}{dt} = kN.$$

The half-lives of certain radioactive isotopes are given in Table 4–2.

Table 4–2
Half-lives of Radioactive Isotopes

Isotope	Decay process	Half-life
H^3	$H^3 \rightarrow He^3 + \beta^-$	12.3 years
C^{14}	$C^{14} \rightarrow N^{14} + \beta^-$	5760 years
P^{32}	$P^{32} \rightarrow S^{32} + \beta^-$	14.3 days
Fe^{55}	$Fe^{55} \rightarrow Mn^{55} + \beta^+$	4.0 years
Co^{60}	$Co^{60} \rightarrow Ni^{60} + \beta^-$	5.2 years
Sr^{90}	$Sr^{90} \rightarrow Y^{90} + \beta^-$	19.9 years
Pu^{239}	$Pu^{239} \rightarrow U^{235} + \alpha$	24,000 years

4–2. EXPERIMENTAL ESTABLISHMENT OF A MORE
COMPLICATED RATE LAW

Additional points regarding the experimental establishment of a rate law are illustrated by the reaction of hypochlorite ion and iodide ion in alkaline solution. The equation for the net reaction is

$$I^- + OCl^- = OI^- + Cl^-.$$

As mentioned in the preceding chapter, the course of this reaction can be followed by spectrophotometric measurements. From plots of light absorption expressed as $\log (I_0/I)$ vs. time, such as Fig. 3–6, values of the reaction rate $d[IO^-]/dt$ can be calculated. Values from

Table 4–3
Dependence of Reaction Rate for
$I^- + OCl^- = Cl^- + OI^-$
upon Concentrations of Iodide Ion and Hypochlorite Ion[a]
$T = 25°C$ 1.00 M NaOH

Time, sec	$[I^-] = [OCl^-]$, mole/liter	$\dfrac{d[OI^-]}{dt} = rate,$ moles/liter/sec	$\dfrac{Rate}{[I^-][OCl^-]}$, liters/mole/sec
0	0.00200		
2	0.00169	1.75×10^{-4}	61
3	0.00158	1.49×10^{-4}	60
4	0.00147	1.26×10^{-4}	58
5	0.00135	1.12×10^{-4}	61
6	0.00123	0.92×10^{-4}	61
8	0.00101	0.62×10^{-4}	61
14	0.00073	0.33×10^{-4}	62

[a] From the work of Y. T. Chia and R. E. Connick, *J. Phys. Chem.* **63,** 1518 (1959).

one particular experiment are given in Table 4–3. The approximate constancy of the quotient $rate/[\text{I}^-][\text{OCl}^-]$ suggests the rate law to be

$$\frac{d[\text{OI}^-]}{dt} = k'[\text{I}^-][\text{OCl}^-],$$

but this conclusion must be considered tentative for two reasons. First, the hydroxide ion concentration does not change during the course of the experiment, and for this reason, the experiment tells nothing about the reaction order with respect to hydroxide ion. Second, the initial concentrations of iodide ion and hypochlorite ion are equal in this experiment. Since they react in 1:1 proportions, the concentrations of iodide ion and hypochlorite ion remain equal to one another as reaction occurs. The last column of Table 4–3 could equally well be headed $rate/[\text{I}^-]^2$ or $rate/[\text{OCl}^-]^2$; the numerical entries in the column would be the same. The point which this illustrates is that only the total reaction order is obtained in an experiment in which the reactants are present in equivalent concentrations. Additional experiments in which the initial concentrations of iodide ion and hypochlorite ion are not equal demonstrate the reaction is first order in iodide ion and first order in hypochlorite ion.

The reaction order with respect to hydroxide ion can be obtained from comparison of experiments run at several different concentrations of hydroxide ion. Results of such experiments are given in Table 4–4. Values of the apparent second-order rate constant obtained in experiments at different concentrations of hydroxide ion are inversely proportional to the concentration of hydroxide ion. A more complete rate law is, therefore,

$$\frac{d[\text{OI}^-]}{dt} = \frac{k[\text{I}^-][\text{OCl}^-]}{[\text{OH}^-]},$$

where k has the value 60 sec^{-1} at 25°C. This rate law does not involve the concentration of water. The order of a reaction with respect to the solvent cannot be established in measurements on relatively dilute solutions; reaction orders can be determined only for substances whose concentrations are varied.

Note that the rate law involves the concentration of hydroxide

Table 4–4

Dependence of the Second-Order Rate Constant Defined by

$$\frac{d[OI^-]}{dt} = k'[I^-][OCl^-]$$

upon the Concentration of Hydroxide Ion[a]

$T = 25°C$

$[OH^-]$, moles/liter	k', liters/mole/sec	$k' \times [OH^-]$, sec^{-1}
1.00	61	61
0.50	120	60
0.25	230	58

[a] From the work of Y. T. Chia and R. E. Connick, *J. Phys. Chem.*, **63**, 1518 (1959).

ion, which does not appear as reactant or product in the balanced equation for the net chemical change:[1]

$$OCl^- + I^- = OI^- + Cl^-.$$

There is no basis in the balanced equation for expecting a dependence of reaction rate upon hydroxide ion. This illustrates the point that the form of a rate law must be established by an experimental study of the reaction rate.

QUESTION:
What is the instantaneous rate of appearance of hypoiodite ion at 25°C in a solution of the composition 0.150 M I$^-$, 0.050 M OCl$^-$, and 0.60 M OH$^-$?
The rate law is

$$\frac{d[OI^-]}{dt} = 60 \ sec^{-1} \frac{[I^-][OCl^-]}{[OH^-]}.$$

[1] The acid dissociation constants for hypochlorous acid and hypoiodous acid are approximately 10^{-8} and 10^{-11}, respectively. In 1 M sodium hydroxide the predominant forms of hypochlorous and hypoiodous acid are, therefore, the anionic species.

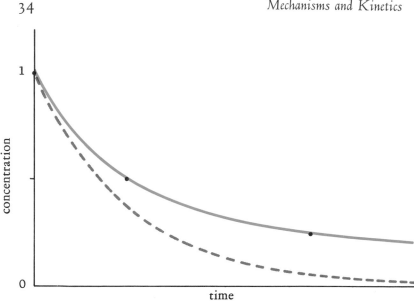

Figure 4–3. Concentration vs. time in a second-order reaction. Successive points are separated by one half-time. (The dashed curve is a first-order reaction with the same rate at $t = 0$.)

Substitution of concentrations gives

$$\frac{d[OI^-]}{dt} = 60 \times \frac{0.150 \times 0.050}{0.60}$$

$$= 0.75 \text{ mole/liter/sec.}$$

We have learned that the half-time of a first-order reaction depends upon the magnitude of the rate constant and not upon the initial concentration. This is not true of second-order reactions nor of reactions of any other orders. The reaction being considered conforms to a second-order rate law in each experiment. Although the data of Table 4–3 are insufficient to show it, this reaction requires 25 sec to go 75 per cent to completion even though it requires only 8.3 sec to go 50 per cent to completion. A first-order reaction requiring 8.3 sec to go 50 per cent to completion would require 2 × 8.3 = 16.6 sec to go 75 per cent to completion. This is shown in Fig. 4–3, a concentration vs. time plot for a second-order reaction. The reaction rate declines more for a second-order reaction as reaction proceeds than for a first-order reaction. Successive half-times are longer and longer as the concentrations decrease.

Just as integral calculus allows transformation of the differential equation for a first-order reaction into an equation relating concentration and time, so also the second-order rate law

$$-\frac{d[A]}{dt} = k[A]^2$$

can be converted to

$$\frac{1}{[A]} = \frac{1}{[A]_0} + kt$$

This equation holds for second-order reactions in which the reactants are present at equivalent concentrations, such as the experiment described in Table 4–3. Figure 4–4 shows a plot of $1/[OCl^-]$ vs. time for these data.

4–3. A TWO-TERM RATE LAW

Each rate law considered in the preceding sections of this chapter consisted of a single term

$$-\frac{d[N_2O_5]}{dt} = k[N_2O_5]$$

and

$$\frac{d[OI^-]}{dt} = k\frac{[I^-][OCl^-]}{[OH^-]}.$$

We shall learn in Chap. 6 that such one-term rate laws are interpreted in terms of a single reaction pathway. Some reactions can occur by more than one pathway, and for such reactions the rate law consists of a sum of terms.

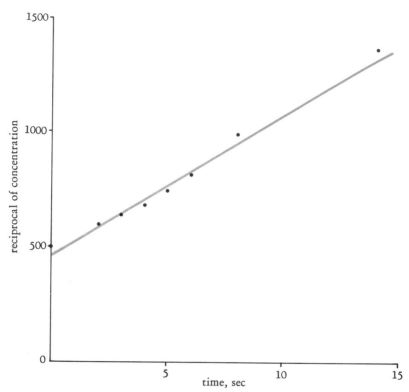

Figure 4–4. Reciprocal of concentration of hypochlorite ion vs. time. Data are from Table 4–3. The approximate linearity proves the reaction is second order in this experiment.

The oxidation of iodide ion by hydrogen peroxide,

$$H_2O_2 + 3I^- + 2H^+ = I_3^- + 2H_2O,$$

occurs by two pathways in acidic solution. In discussing this reaction, some attention will be paid to a particularly simple method by which the rate can be determined. The average rate at which this reaction occurs is inversely proportional to the time required for a particular amount of triiodide ion to form:

$$\text{average rate} = \frac{\Delta[I_3^-]}{\Delta t}.$$

If $\Delta[I_3^-]$ is the same in every experiment,

$$\text{average rate} \propto (\Delta t)^{-1}.$$

If the developing color of triiodide ion in reaction mixtures of varying composition is compared with the color of a standard in which there is some particular concentration of triiodide, the time at which the intensity of color of the reaction mixture is the same as that of the standard can be noted. This is the value of Δt in the above formulation. During this time interval, the concentrations of hydrogen ion, hydrogen peroxide, and iodide ion change, but with an appropriately low concentration of triiodide ion in the standard, the changes of reactant concentrations are small and it is possible to correlate the values of $(\Delta t)^{-1}$ with the average concentrations existing during the time interval in question. (Experiments of this type may be done as a lecture demonstration or by students in an elementary laboratory.) For studies at moderate acidity ($[H^+] > 0.5\ M$), the correlation observed is approximately

$$(\Delta t)^{-1} \propto [H^+][H_2O_2][I^-].$$

In acetic acid solution ($[H^+] \cong 10^{-3}$), the reaction rate does not depend upon concentration of hydrogen ion:

$$(\Delta t)^{-1} \propto [H_2O_2][I^-].$$

These two limiting forms of the rate law can be combined into a single rate law. The sum of two terms

$$\frac{d[I_3^-]}{dt} = k[H_2O_2][I^-] + k'[H^+][H_2O_2][I^-]$$

is the only satisfactory combination which correlates the rate and reactant concentrations over the entire range of hydrogen ion concentration. More elaborate experiments than the simple ones outlined here confirm this rate law, and at 25°C the experiments yield values of $k = 1.15 \times 10^{-2}$ liter/mole/sec and $k' = 1.75 \times 10^{-1}$ liter^2/moles^2/sec. A two-term rate law of this sort indicates that reaction is occurring via two different reaction pathways. The magnitude of each term gives the amount of triiodide ion produced via each pathway.

PROBLEM:

Using the values of k and k' given above, calculate the concentration of hydrogen ion at which the rate of production of triiodide ion via each of the two pathways is the same.

For the total rate to be made up of equal contributions from the two terms,

$$k[H_2O_2][I^-] = k'[H^+][H_2O_2][I^-].$$

Therefore,

$$[H^+] = \frac{k}{k'}.$$

Therefore, at 25°C,

$$[H^+] = \frac{1.15 \times 10^{-2}}{1.75 \times 10^{-1}} \text{ mole/liter,}$$

or

$$[H^+] = 0.066\ M.$$

At 0.066 M hydrogen ion, each reaction pathway contributes equally to the total reaction rate.

Since the balanced equation includes hydrogen ion as a reactant, the concentration of hydrogen ion decreases as reaction proceeds. The change during a particular experiment depends, of course, upon the relative values of initial concentrations of reactants. The presence of an appropriate buffer system made up of a weak acid and its conjugate base minimizes the change in acidity during an experiment.

Figure 4–5 shows the varying dependence of reaction rate upon the concentration of hydrogen ion and also the contribution of each pathway to the total reaction rate.

If studies were confined to solutions in which the concentration of hydrogen ion was less than $\sim$0.001 M, the single-term rate law

$$\frac{d[I_3^-]}{dt} = k[H_2O_2][I^-]$$

would be consistent with the data. There would be no suggestion that at higher acidity an additional term is necessary to correlate the rate data. This general limitation should be recognized. Extension of the concentration range may make new reaction pathways more important and therefore make the corresponding rate law terms more important.

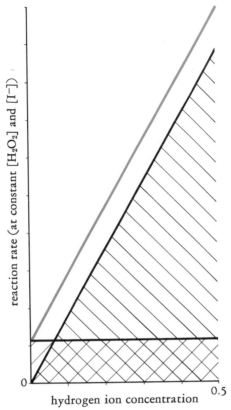

reaction rate (at constant $[H_2O_2]$ and $[I^-]$)

0

hydrogen ion concentration   0.5

Figure 4–5. The contribution of each term of the rate law to reaction rate. Colored line, total rate; \\\\\\\\ **contribution of term $k'[H^+][H_2O_2][I^-]$;** ///// **contribution of term $k[H_2O_2][I^-]$.**

PROBLEMS

1. The rate law for the reaction

$$Cr(OH_2)_6^{3+} + SCN^- = Cr(OH_2)_5NCS^{2+} + H_2O$$

occurring in the forward direction is

$$\frac{d[\mathrm{Cr(OH_2)_5NCS^{2+}}]}{dt} = [\mathrm{Cr(OH_2)_6^{3+}}][\mathrm{SCN^-}]\left\{k + \frac{k'}{[\mathrm{H^+}]} + \frac{k''}{[\mathrm{H^+}]^2}\right\}$$

(a) By how many independent pathways does this reaction occur?
(b) The values of k and k' at 25°C are 1.9×10^{-6} liter/mole/sec and 7.2×10^{-9} sec^{-1}, respectively. At what concentration of hydrogen ion are rates by the pathways corresponding to these two terms equal?

2. Quenching a reaction mixture by dilution with solvent of the same temperature is effective only for reactions of certain reaction orders. What statement can you make regarding this point?

3. A reactant A decomposes in a first-order reaction. Starting with equations given in the text or on a more intuitive basis, derive the equation

$$\frac{[\mathrm{A}]_t}{[\mathrm{A}]_0} = \left(\frac{1}{2}\right)^n$$

where $[\mathrm{A}]_0$ and $[\mathrm{A}]_t$ are concentrations of A at zero time and at time t, and n is the number of half-times the reaction has run at time t.

4. From the data on the rate of decomposition of dinitrogen pentoxide given in Chap. 4, the rate constant for the rate law

$$\frac{-d[\mathrm{N_2O_5}]}{dt} = k[\mathrm{N_2O_5}]$$

has the value $k = 6.2 \times 10^{-4}$ min^{-1} at 45°C. In a dilute solution the reaction product nitrogen dioxide is present predominantly as monomeric $\mathrm{NO_2}$. The rate law can be written

$$\frac{d[\mathrm{NO_2}]}{dt} = k'[\mathrm{N_2O_5}].$$

What is the value of the rate constant k' at this same temperature?
(Ans.: $k' = 1.24 \times 10^{-3}$ min^{-1})

5. In this chapter, a rate law involving two independent terms was given. In Prob. 1 (above), there is a rate law involving three independent terms. In each of these rate laws it is the order with respect to hydrogen ion which is different in the several terms. How does the apparent order of each of these reactions with respect to hydrogen ion change as the hydrogen ion concentration becomes larger?

V

Theories of Reaction Kinetics

Chemical reactions of gaseous substances occur in appropriate collisions of reactant molecules, as pictured in Fig. 2–2. Not all collisions are appropriate collisions.

5–1. GAS-PHASE REACTIONS

Before considering what is required for a collision to be appropriate for reaction, let us consider the kinetic molecular theory of gases which allows calculation of the average collision frequency of gaseous molecules. This collision frequency includes both collisions appropriate for reaction and collisions inappropriate for reaction. It represents, therefore, an upper limit of the reaction rate.

Kinetic-Molecular Theory and Bimolecular Collision Frequency

As the reader may recall, the kinetic-molecular theory is based on the postulate that molecules of a gas are in constant motion and collide with one another and with walls of the container. These collisions with the container are responsible for the pressure exerted by a gas on the interior walls of its container. With this simple a start, it is possible to derive a relationship between the average kinetic energy of gaseous molecules and the product of the pressure P which they exert on walls of a container of volume V. The result is

$$PV = \tfrac{2}{3}n'(\tfrac{1}{2}m\overline{v^2}) = \tfrac{2}{3}n'(\overline{E_k}) \qquad (5\text{-}1)$$

where n' is the number of molecules, m is the mass of each molecule, $\overline{v^2}$ is the average of the squares of velocities of the molecules, and $\overline{E_k}$ is the average kinetic energy of the molecules. This theoretical equation (5–1) and the empirical combined Boyle-Charles law

$$PV = nRT, \qquad (5\text{-}2)$$

where n is the number of moles of gas, R is a proportionality constant called the gas constant, and T is the absolute temperature, are both equations for the product PV. If the right-hand sides of the two equations are equated, the result is

$$\tfrac{2}{3}n'\overline{E_k} = nRT,$$

which gives us

$$\overline{E_k} = \frac{3}{2}\frac{n}{n'}\, RT$$
$$= \frac{3}{2}\frac{R}{N}\, T$$
$$= \frac{3}{2}\, kT, \qquad (5\text{-}3)$$

where N is Avogadro's number, 6.02×10^{23} molecules/mole. The gas constant divided by Avogadro's number, $R/N = k$, is called the Boltzmann constant. Equation (5–3) shows a direct proportionality between average kinetic energy of gaseous molecules and the absolute temperature of the gas. This equation gives the fundamental meaning of temperature: the absolute temperature of a gas is a measure of the average kinetic energy of its molecules.

Before we continue to derive the average collision frequency of gaseous molecules, notice the dimensions and magnitude of the gas constant R. The equation relating $\overline{E_k}$ and T indicates the gas constant has dimensions of energy/deg/mole. The numerical value of R depends upon the units in which energy is expressed. If we remember that 1 mole of a perfect gas occupies 22,400 cm^3 at 1 atm pressure at 273.15°K, we can calculate the value of the gas constant as follows:

$$R = \frac{PV}{nT} = \frac{1 \text{ atm} \times 2.24 \times 10^4 \text{ cm}^3}{1 \text{ mole} \times 273.15 \text{ deg}}$$

$$= 82.1 \text{ cm}^3\text{-atm/deg/mole.}$$

Solution of gas law problems is made particularly convenient by using R expressed in this set of dimensions.

The equation for the average of the squares of velocities of gaseous molecules is

$$\overline{v^2} = \frac{3RT}{Nm} = \frac{3RT}{M}, \tag{5-4}$$

where M is the weight of 1 mole of the gas $(M = mN)$. The value of R must be expressed in the more fundamental cgs (centimeter-gram-second) units if this equation is to be used to calculate $\overline{v^2}$. This can be done by converting the dimensions of pressure from 1 atm to cgs units. Remembering that 1 atm pressure is defined as the pressure exerted by a column of mercury (density = 13.6 g/cm³) 76.0 cm high at a place where the acceleration of gravity is 980.665 cm/sec², one can evaluate the gas constant:

$$R = 82.1 \text{ cm}^3\text{-atm/deg/mole} \times (13.6 \text{ g/cm}^3$$
$$\times 76.0 \text{ cm} \times 980.7 \text{ cm/sec}^2)/\text{atm}$$
$$= 8.31 \times 10^7 \text{ g-cm}^2/\text{sec}^2/\text{deg/mole.}$$

(Since 1 g-cm²/sec² = 1 erg and 10^7 ergs = 1 joule, $R = 8.31$ joules/deg/mole.) We have, therefore, an equation

$$\overline{v^2} = 3 \times 8.31 \times 10^7 \frac{T}{M} \text{ cm}^2/\text{sec}^2$$

$$\overline{v^2} = 2.49 \times 10^8 \frac{T}{M} \text{ cm}^2/\text{sec}^2 \tag{5-5}$$

with which the average of the squares of velocities of gaseous molecules can be calculated. By taking the square root of each side of this equation, one obtains a quantity called the root-mean-square velocity.[1]

---

[1] The reader may find it informative to compare the average age of members of his family with the square root of the average of the squares of those ages. The relative values of these two quantities depend upon the distribution of ages within the family.

$$(\overline{v^2})^{1/2} = 1.58 \times 10^4 \left(\frac{T}{M}\right)^{1/2} cm/sec.$$

The relationship between average velocity and root-mean-square velocity is derived from the theory of the distribution of molecular velocities. Although results of this theory will be used, the theory itself is beyond the scope of this treatment. The average molecular velocity $\bar{v}$ is $(8/3\pi)^{1/2}$ times the root-mean-square velocity $(\overline{v^2})^{1/2}$; it can be calculated from

$$\bar{v} = \left(\frac{8}{3\pi}\right)^{1/2} (\overline{v^2})^{1/2}.$$

Therefore

$$\bar{v} = \left(\frac{8RT}{\pi M}\right)^{1/2}$$

$$= 1.455 \times 10^4 \left(\frac{T}{M}\right)^{1/2} cm/sec. \qquad (5\text{--}6)$$

Average velocities of certain gaseous molecules at 298.2°K are given in Table 5–1. The relative velocities of hydrogen, hydrogen fluoride, and chlorine are illustrated in Fig. 5–1, which shows that molecules collide with one another more frequently, the more rapidly they are moving.

Table 5-1
Gas-Molecule Velocities
298.2°K

	M	$\bar{v}$	
		cm/sec	*miles/hr*
H_2	2.016	17.7×10^4	3960
HF	20.0	5.60×10^4	1260
Cl_2	71.0	2.98×10^4	668
I_2	253.8	1.58×10^4	354

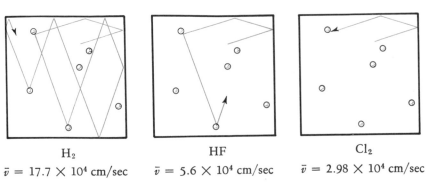

$$\bar{v} = 17.7 \times 10^4 \text{ cm/sec} \qquad \bar{v} = 5.6 \times 10^4 \text{ cm/sec} \qquad \bar{v} = 2.98 \times 10^4 \text{ cm/sec}$$

($\bar{v}$ values at 298.2°K)

Figure 5–1. The relative velocities of H_2 ($M = 2$), HF ($M = 20$), and Cl_2 ($M = 71$). The length of path is proportional to the average velocity; it shows the relative distance traveled in a unit of time. The greater this distance, the larger the number of collisions the molecule makes, both with the walls and with other molecules (shown as circles).

But before molecular collisions can be discussed, the size of molecules must be introduced. Two molecules collide if they come within a distance of σ, the molecular diameter, of one another:

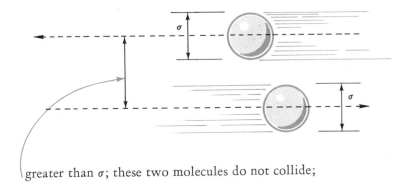

greater than σ; these two molecules do not collide;

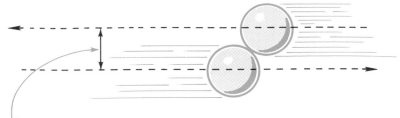

less than σ; these two molecules do collide.

The larger the value of σ, the greater the probability that two molecules will collide. The collision of two molecules, each of diameter σ, can be considered equivalent to the collision of a molecule with radius σ and another molecule represented as a point. In each representation, collision is judged to have occurred if centers of the molecules come within a distance σ of one another. Calculation of collision frequency is simpler if based upon the second representation. The average collision frequency for pairs of molecules in a gas is approximately equal to the total number of point molecules in the volume swept out in unit time by a molecule of radius σ moving with its average velocity, as illustrated in Fig. 5–2. A molecule sweeps through a cylinder $\bar{v}$ cm long in 1 sec. For a molecule with $\sigma = 3.5 \times 10^{-8}$ cm and molecular weight 130, the volume of this cylinder at 500°C (773°K) is

$$V = \pi r^2 l = \pi \sigma^2 \bar{v}$$

$$= \pi(3.5 \times 10^{-8})^2 \left[1.455 \times 10^4 \left(\frac{773}{130} \right)^{1/2} \right]$$

$$= 1.37 \times 10^{-10} \text{ cm}^3.$$

If the concentration of gaseous molecules is 10^{-3} mole/liter, there are in this volume 10^{-6} mole/cm^3 $\times$ 1.37 $\times$ 10^{-10} cm^3 $\times$ 6.02 $\times$ 10^{23} molecules/mole = 8.2 $\times$ 10^7 molecules. This is the number of collisions which the one molecule in question makes in 1 sec, based upon the assumption that all other molecules are stationary. If motion of all molecules is taken into account, the calculation is more complicated; the result of the correct calculation is a $\sqrt{2}$-fold higher collision frequency. The total frequency of collisions of pairs of molecules in a liter of gas is obtained by multiplying the collision frequency for one molecule by the number of molecules in

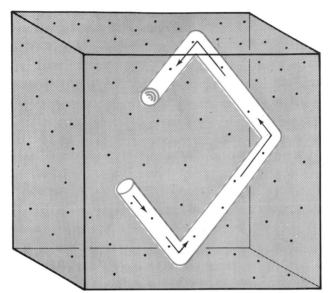

Figure 5-2. Collisions of a moving molecule of radius σ with stationary point molecules. In the volume swept out by the moving molecule there are eleven point molecules. This is the number of collisions in the time interval in question, according to this simple model.

a liter and then dividing by 2, since each collision of two molecules has been counted twice in this approach. For molecules with $\sigma = 3.5 \times 10^{-8}$ cm and molecular weight 130 at a concentration of 10^{-3} mole/liter, the collision frequency per liter at 500°C is, therefore,

$$\text{collision frequency} = \tfrac{1}{2} \times \sqrt{2} \times 8.2 \times 10^7 \times 10^{-3} \times 6.02 \times 10^{23}$$

$$= 3.5 \times 10^{28} \text{ collisions/liter/sec.}$$

If the molecules reacted upon every collision, this collision frequency would be the reaction rate. In more familiar terms, this rate is

$$\frac{3.5 \times 10^{28}}{6.0 \times 10^{23}} = 5.8 \times 10^4 \text{ moles/liter/sec,}$$

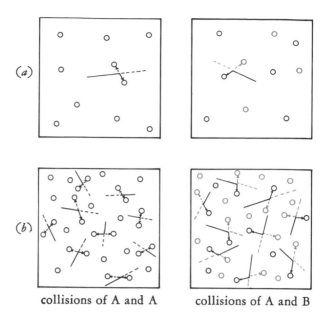

collisions of A and A   collisions of A and B

Figure 5–3. Dependence of collision frequency upon concentration. In each case the collision frequency increases by a factor of 9 in going from (a) to (b). For collisions of A and A, this results from a threefold increase in concentration of A. For collisions of A and B, this results from twofold increase in concentration of A and a 4.5-fold increase in concentration of B.

certainly a very high value. This is the instantaneous value of the rate at this concentration if reaction occurred upon every collision.

In this calculation of the total number of collisions of two molecules in 1 liter in 1 sec, the concentration of the gas appeared as a factor twice. The frequency of collisions of two gaseous molecules of the same kind is proportional to the square of the concentration of the gas:

$$\text{collision frequency} \propto [A]^2.$$

A reexamination of the derivation will indicate that the collision frequency of two gaseous molecules of different kinds is proportional to the product of the concentrations of each gas:

$$\text{collision frequency} \propto [A][B]$$

(Fig. 5–3). We conclude, therefore, that a second-order rate law will be associated with a gas-phase reaction which goes by a mechanism consisting of bimolecular collisions. Notice the usage of the terms "second order" and "bimolecular." The two are not synonyms. The reaction order pertains to the number of concentration factors in the experimentally established rate law; the molecularity pertains to the number of species taking part in a postulated reaction step. Although it might seem that reaction order and molecularity must be uniquely associated, later discussion will show that assumption of a compulsory relationship is unwarranted.

The Temperature Coefficient of Reaction Velocity

Now let us compare the calculated collision frequency with an actual rate for a reaction which proceeds by a single bimolecular step. The decomposition of hydrogen iodide is such a reaction. The net chemical reaction is

$$2HI = H_2 + I_2,$$

and the rate of decomposition at a great distance from equilibrium[1] is given by the second-order rate law

$$\frac{d[I_2]}{dt} = k[HI]^2.$$

The numerical values of molecular weight and collision diameter used in the model calculation are appropriate for direct comparison with the observed rate of decomposition of hydrogen iodide ($M = 127.9$). At 500°C and a concentration of 10^{-3} mole/liter, the rate

---

[1] The study of this reaction generally is carried out under conditions such that both forward and reverse reaction must be considered. From such studies the rate of decomposition in the absence of recombination can be obtained. This is given by the rate law being considered.

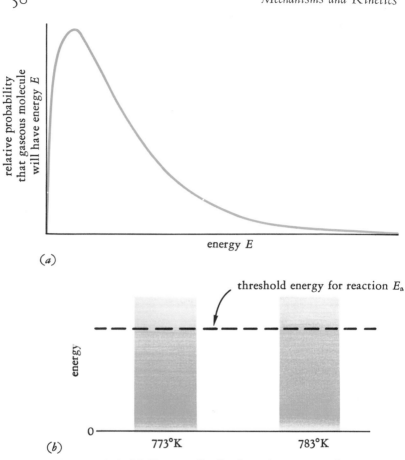

Figure 5–4. (*a*) **Energy distribution of gaseous molecules at 773°K.** (*b*) **Schematic representation of energy distribution of gaseous molecules at 773 and 783°K. The density of color represents the relative numbers of molecules.**

of this reaction is 1.2×10^{-8} mole/liter/sec, which is $\sim (5 \times 10^{12})$-fold lower than the value expected if every collision were effective.

A clue to the ineffectiveness of collisions of hydrogen iodide molecules in leading to decomposition into hydrogen and iodine is provided by the sensitivity of reaction rate to temperature. For an increase in temperature of 10°, from 500 to 510°C, the reaction rate by the bimolecular pathway goes up by 44 per cent. The average molecular velocity is proportioned to $T^{1/2}$ and increases by only 0.6 per cent with this 10° increase of temperatuture:

$$\frac{\bar{v}_2}{\bar{v}_1} = \left(\frac{T_2}{T_1}\right)^{1/2} = \left(\frac{510 + 273}{500 + 273}\right)^{1/2}$$

$$= 1.006.$$

The increase in collision frequency cannot, therefore, cause the large observed increase in reaction rate. Although the average molecular velocity shows only this mild dependence upon temperature, the fraction of molecules with relatively high energies increases dramatically with increasing temperature. This is shown in Fig. 5–4, in which the energy distribution of gaseous molecules at 773°K is represented graphically and schematically. These figures show that relatively small numbers of molecules have high kinetic energies. If only molecules with large amounts of energy are capable of reacting upon collision, the reaction rate is much smaller than the collision frequency. Schematic representations of the energy distribution at the two temperatures 773 and 783°K show that a 10° increase in temperature causes a large increase in relative number of very energetic molecules, which produces the large increase in rate.

The exact form of theoretical equation which one derives for the temperature dependence of a second-order rate constant depends upon the exact prerequisites which one assumes must be satisfied for reaction to occur. If reaction occurs in a collision only if the relative translational energy along the line of centers of the two molecules at the moment of impact is in excess of ΔE_a, called the activation energy, the rate constant should have the form

$$k = pZe^{-\Delta E_a/RT}, \tag{5-7}$$

where T is the absolute temperature, Z is the total collision frequency (calculated earlier in this chapter), and p is called the steric factor. The value of p is less than unity if some special orientation of colliding molecules is necessary, in addition to an energy requirement, for reaction to occur. The meaning of p can be illustrated by consideration of collision of hydrogen iodide molecules. If two hydrogen iodide molecules collide with the orientation

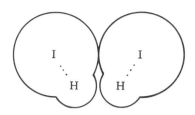

and with sufficient energy, hydrogen and iodine form; if, however, the orientation of colliding molecules is

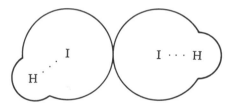

they simply will bounce off one another. The numerical value of p for the hydrogen iodide decomposition is found to be ~0.2. The numerical value of p for reactions of more complicated molecules may be very much lower than unity. In some more elaborate theories, low values of p are interpreted to reflect factors other than steric. Equations of slightly different form from Eq. (5–7) are derived by assuming slightly different sets of prerequisites for reaction; all, however, contain the exponential term $e^{-\Delta E_a/RT}$ as a factor.

The value of ΔE_a can be obtained from experimental values of the rate constant as a function of temperature. By taking the logarithm of each side of Eq. (5–7), one obtains

$$\log k = \log pZ - \frac{\Delta E_a}{2.3RT} .$$

Data conforming to this equation give an essentially linear plot of the logarithm of the rate constant vs. the reciprocal of the tem-

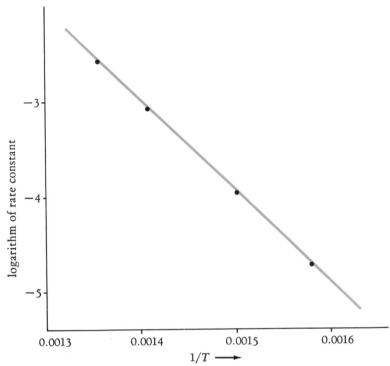

Figure 5–5. A plot of log k vs. $1/T$ for the reaction

$$2HI \xrightarrow{k} H_2 + I_2$$

The slope of this line is equal to $-\Delta E_a/(2.3R)$. The value of ΔE_a is, therefore, equal to $-2.3R \times$ slope. [Data from the work of J. H. Sullivan, *J. Chem. Phys.*, **30**, 1292 (1959).]

perature.[1] Values of the second-order rate constant for decomposition of hydrogen iodide at 633, 667, 710, and 738°K are so plotted in Fig. 5–5. From the slope of this line, the value of ΔE_a is calculated to be 43.7 kcal/mole.

---

[1] In a more rigorous treatment of the temperature coefficient of bimolecular reactions, account would be taken of the very slight dependence of the total collision frequency Z upon the temperature.

Even before the kinetic molecular theory had developed to such a point that it could be used to derive Eq. (5–7), plots such as Fig. 5–5 were made in the correlation of kinetic data. Svante Arrhenius (1859–1927) made use of such plots, and he first recognized their general significance. In the form

$$k = Ae^{-\Delta E_a/RT} \tag{5-8}$$

the equation for the temperature dependence of a rate constant is called the Arrhenius equation. It is applied to experimental data for reaction of all orders. Theoretical treatment indicates the activation energy ΔE_a obtained from use of Eq. (5–8) applied to reactions of other orders has a significance analogous to that already indicated for bimolecular reactions.

The activation energy for a reaction can be calculated directly from values of rate constants measured at two different temperatures:

at T_1

$$\ln k_1 = \ln A - \frac{\Delta E_a}{RT_1},$$

and at T_2

$$\ln k_2 = \ln A - \frac{\Delta E_a}{RT_2}.$$

Subtraction of these two equations yields

$$\ln \frac{k_1}{k_2} = \frac{\Delta E_a}{R} \left(\frac{1}{T_2} - \frac{1}{T_1} \right).$$

which, upon rearrangement and conversion to logarithms to the base 10 ($\ln k = 2.3 \log k$), gives

$$\Delta E_a = \frac{2.3RT_1T_2}{T_1 - T_2} \log \frac{k_1}{k_2}. \tag{5-9}$$

EXAMPLE:

The reaction of hexaaquochromium(III) ion and thiocyanate ion to form a complex ion,

$$Cr(OH_2)_6^{3+} + SCN^- = Cr(OH_2)_5NCS^{2+} + H_2O,$$

proceeds by several pathways. The rate law term corresponding to one path is

$$\frac{d[\text{Cr(OH}_2)_5\text{NCS}^{2+}]}{dt} = k[\text{Cr(OH}_2)_6{}^{3+}][\text{SCN}^-].$$

The value of k is 2.0×10^{-6} liter/mole/sec at 14°C and 2.2×10^{-5} liter/mole/sec at 30°C. What is the value of ΔE_a?

$$\Delta E_a = \frac{2.3 \times 1.99 \text{ cal/mole/deg} \times 287° \times 303°}{16°} \log \frac{2.2 \times 10^{-5}}{2.0 \times 10^{-6}}$$

$$= 26.0 \text{ kcal/mole.}$$

This reaction is very slow relative to most complex ion formation reactions. At concentrations of 0.05 M thiocyanate ion and 0.001 M chromium(III), formation of monothiocyanatopenta-aquochromium(III) is essentially a first-order reaction since the concentration of thiocyanate ion does not change appreciably as reaction occurs. The apparent first-order rate constant is $k[\text{SCN}^-]$, and, therefore, at 14°C the half-time for the reaction is

$$t_{1/2} = \frac{0.69}{k[\text{SCN}^-]} = \frac{0.69}{2.0 \times 10^{-6} \times 0.05} \text{ sec}$$

$$= 6.9 \times 10^6 \text{ sec. or 80 days.}$$

This slowness is characteristic of displacement reactions of chromium(III).

In many elementary books, one finds the generalization that a 10° increase in temperature causes rates of homogeneous reactions to double. Applied to a reaction at 300°K, this corresponds to an activation energy of

$$\Delta E_a = \frac{2.3 \times 1.99 \text{ cal/mole/deg} \times 295° \times 305°}{10°} \log 2$$

$$= 12.4 \text{ kcal/mole.}$$

In complete absence of relevant experimental data, this generalization may have some usefulness; but reliance on it is very risky, since the activation energies for many, many reactions do not lie close to 12.4 kcal/mole. The two reactions already cited, one in the gas phase and the other in aqueous solution, are examples of reactions which do not conform to the generalization.

In the bimolecular reaction of two hydrogen iodide molecules,

with an activation energy of 43.7 kcal/mole, the covalent bonds in
two moles of hydrogen iodide are broken.   If the product of the
bimolecular reaction were uncombined atoms, the reaction would be
very endothermic[1]:

$$2HI = 2H + 2I \qquad \Delta H = 141 \text{ kcal.}$$

One might wonder how collisions involving only 43.7 kcal/mole
could accomplish the necessary bond disruption.   Also involved in
the net chemical change, however, is formation of covalent bonds
between hydrogen atoms in molecular hydrogen and between iodine
atoms in molecular iodine.   In the bimolecular pathway for this
reaction, the molecules are believed to go through the intermediate
configuration

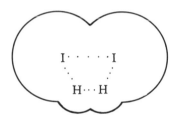

in which dashed lines represent some sort of partial bonding.   The
bond between the hydrogen atoms and the bond between iodine
atoms form as the bonds in the two hydrogen iodide molecules
break.   At no time in the process are uncombined hydrogen atoms
and uncombined iodine atoms produced, and it is not necessary,
therefore, for an effective collision to involve the amount of 141
kcal/mole.

The reaction pathway by which two hydrogen iodide molecules
actually react to form hydrogen and iodine is a minimum-energy
pathway, Fig. 5–6.   By this is meant that the two hydrogen iodide
molecules come together to form the intermediate configuration

---

[1] A positive sign for ΔH means the products have greater heat content than the
reactants.   This much heat must be added to reactants to convert them to products
at the same temperature.

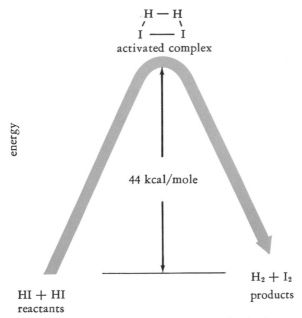

H — H
I ——— I
activated complex

energy

44 kcal/mole

HI + HI
reactants

H₂ + I₂
products

Figure 5–6. Minimum-energy pathway for hydrogen iodide decomposition. The atomic configuration of maximum energy on this pathway is the activated complex.

pictured above by the route requiring the smallest expenditure of energy. Along this minimum-energy pathway, there is a configuration of maximum energy. For the reaction under consideration, this is the four-membered ring configuration already pictured. This configuration of atoms corresponding to the maximum energy in the minimum-energy pathway is called the *activated complex* or the *transition state*. The activated complex is often designated by a dagger symbol ‡; for the hydrogen iodide decomposition by the bimolecular pathway, the activated complex has the formula $H_2I_2{}^\ddagger$.

Energetics for a system of 2 g-atoms of hydrogen and 2 g-atoms of iodine are shown in Fig. 5–7. To get from molecular hydrogen iodide to molecular hydrogen and molecular iodine, a state of very slightly higher energy, the system must go through the configuration

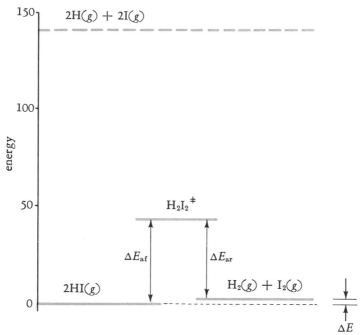

Figure 5–7. A graphical comparison of the energy of 2 moles $HI(g)$; 1 mole $H_2(g)$ plus 1 mole $I_2(g)$; 1 mole $H_2I_2^{\ddagger}$ (activated complex); and 2 moles $H(g)$ plus 2 moles $I(g)$. (In order of increasing energy content.)

of the activated complex, which has a very much greater energy. The separated atoms are at a still higher state of energy.

The energies represented in Fig. 5–7 are equally pertinent for the reaction of hydrogen and iodine to form hydrogen iodide. The activated complex shown on page 56 has the same geometry and energy whether it is an activated complex for the reaction

$$2HI \rightarrow H_2 + I_2$$

or for the reaction

$$H_2 + I_2 \rightarrow 2HI.$$

In the former activated complex, two hydrogen-iodine bonds are breaking and a hydrogen-hydrogen bond and an iodine-iodine bond are forming. In the latter activated complex, a hydrogen-hydrogen bond and an iodine-iodine bond are breaking and two hydrogen-iodine bonds are forming.

Figure 5–7 shows the relationship between the energies of activation for the forward and reverse reactions and the energy difference between products and reactants. Since the over-all reaction

$$2HI = H_2 + I_2$$

is slightly endothermic, $\Delta H = +3$ kcal/mole, the activation energy for reaction of hydrogen and iodine is 3 kcal/mole less than that for reaction of hydrogen iodide:

$$\Delta E = \Delta E_{af} - \Delta E_{ar},$$

where ΔE is the change in energy in the over-all reaction and ΔE_{af} and ΔE_{ar} are activation energies for the forward and reverse reactions. (For a gaseous reaction in which there are the same number of molecules on reactant and product side of the balanced equation, $\Delta E = \Delta H$.)

These relationships of the forward and reverse reactions illustrate an important point. *A pathway for a forward reaction must also be a pathway for the reverse of the reaction. At equilibrium in a reaction occurring by more than one pathway, the forward and reverse rates are equal along each pathway.* These are statements of the *principle of microscopic reversibility*.

Contrasting Kinetics of Decomposition of Complex and Simple Molecules

Decomposition of some complicated molecules occurs in an elementary reaction, but many complicated molecules decompose by a pathway consisting of a sequence of reactions. It is appropriate to compare the reaction order for reactions in the first of these categories with the reaction order in decomposition of simple molecules. Decomposition of simple gaseous molecules (e.g., hydrogen iodide) at moderate pressures is a second-order reaction, but decomposition of a complex molecule may be first order. As an example, decomposition of cyclopentene to give hydrogen and cyclopentadiene,

follows the rate law

$$-\frac{d[\text{cyclopentene}]}{dt} = k[\text{cyclopentene}],$$

and has an activation energy of 58.8 kcal/mole. In contrast, decomposition of simple molecules in the gas phase is not governed by a first-order rate law at moderate pressures. This contrasting kinetic pattern for decomposition of complex molecules and simple molecules is explained by consideration of the vibration of these molecules.

We already know that only molecules with energies above a certain critical amount react, and we further know that molecular collisions provide this energy. But a molecular collision involves two molecules, and the rate of such collisions is proportional to the second power of the concentration. In spite of this, decomposition of a complex molecule may be governed by a first-order rate law. The energized complex molecule does not decompose until this requisite energy is localized in the appropriate molecular vibrations. This takes time; on the average, the complicated molecule must undergo many vibrational motions before sufficient energy becomes localized where it is required for decomposition. If the energized molecule

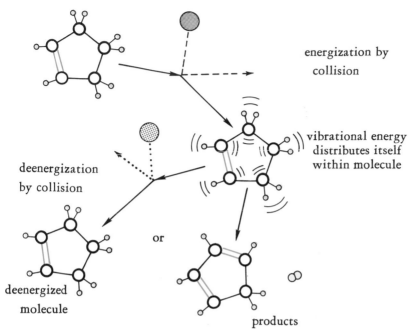

energization by
collision

vibrational energy
distributes itself
within molecule

deenergization
by collision

or

deenergized
molecule

products

Figure 5–8. Decomposition of a complex molecule, cyclopentene.

suffers a collision before decomposition, the most probable fate of the molecule is loss of energy, Fig. 5–8. If sufficient energy is lost, the molecule is no longer capable of reacting. Since both energization and deenergization processes are bimolecular, the *fraction* of molecules with energies above the critical energy does not depend upon the concentration of the gas. The rate of decomposition is proportional to the concentration of energized molecules, which in turn is proportional to the first power of the total concentration of the substance. The rate of decomposition conforms, therefore, to a first-order rate law. For a complex molecule, except at very low pressures, the energized molecules are at their equilibrium concentration, this low equilibrium concentration being maintained by energizing and deenergizing collisions.

At low enough pressures, even decomposition of a relatively complex molecule may be governed by a second-order rate law because at the very low pressure the collision frequency is inadequate to maintain an equilibrium concentration of energized molecules. At such low pressures, the most probable fate of an energized molecule is decomposition, because relatively long time intervals elapse between collisions. Before a deactivating collision occurs, the molecule decomposes. The actual pressure range over which the reaction order changes from second to first depends upon the complexity of the molecule.

For a simple molecule, decomposition follows almost immediately after the collision by which the activation energy was provided. In the limiting case of a diatomic molecule, the only molecular vibration in which energy can be stored corresponds to the same motion that leads to decomposition if the vibration is of sufficient amplitude. If a molecular collision provides sufficient energy to a simple molecule, decomposition occurs before a deactivating collision takes place. The rate of decomposition depends, therefore, upon the frequency of activating collisions, and decomposition of a simple molecule A is governed by a second-order rate law:

$$-\frac{d[A]}{dt} = k[A][M].$$

The chemical nature of M, a substance present in large excess and with which the reactant is most likely to make an activating collision, is not of primary importance. In general, polyatomic molecules are more efficient than noble gases in the role of activating a molecule for decomposition. In the absence of a foreign gas, the reactant itself fills this role and the rate law is

$$-\frac{d[A]}{dt} = k[A]^2.$$

An example of a second-order decomposition of a simple molecule in the presence of a foreign gas is one of the pathways for decomposition of nitrogen dioxide in the presence of argon, Fig. 5-9. The net chemical change is

$$2NO_2 = 2NO + O_2.$$

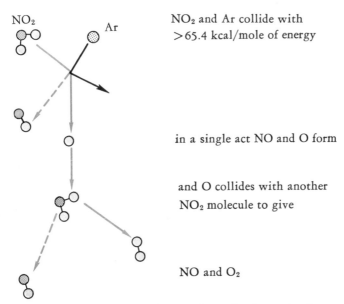

NO$_2$ and Ar collide with
> 65.4 kcal/mole of energy

in a single act NO and O form

and O collides with another
NO$_2$ molecule to give

NO and O$_2$

Figure 5–9. Decomposition of a simple molecule, nitrogen dioxide.

The rate-law term corresponding to the pathway being considered is

$$-\frac{d[NO_2]}{dt} = k[NO_2][Ar]$$

from which it is inferred that the rate of the bimolecular process

$$NO_2 + Ar \rightarrow NO + O + Ar$$

is that to which the measured rate is proportional. The activation energy for this reaction in which a bond breaks but none forms is relatively high, 65.4 kcal/mole. Reaction pathways with this high an activation energy usually have appreciable rates only at high temperatures; the study being discussed here was conducted in the temperature range 1400 to 2300°K. This one process does not, of course, accomplish the net chemical change. The rapid step which follows and completes the over-all reaction is believed to be

$$O + NO_2 \rightarrow O_2 + NO.$$

Since this rapid reaction consumes an additional molecule of nitrogen dioxide, the rate constant of the empirical rate law is twofold larger than the rate constant for the bimolecular rate-determining process

$$NO_2 + Ar \rightarrow NO + O + Ar.$$

A total of two molecules of nitrogen dioxide is consumed for each occurrence of the rate-determining step.

Related to the necessity that dissociation of a diatomic molecule be a second-order reaction is the necessity that recombination of atoms to form a diatomic molecule be a third-order reaction. Chapter 9 includes discussion of an experimental method by which the very rapid recombination of iodine atoms can be studied. This recombination,

$$2I = I_2,$$

does not actually occur in a simple bimolecular step. If two iodine atoms come together in a bimolecular collision, the bond energy of 36 kcal/mole is liberated if an iodine molecule forms. The iodine molecule has no extra degrees of vibrational freedom in which this energy can reside. There is no place for the energy to go if only two iodine atoms are involved in the collision. Two iodine atoms upon bimolecular collision will simply bounce off one another. If, however, a third body is involved in the collision, it may depart with extra kinetic energy and leave the combination of two iodine atoms with less than enough energy to break the newly formed bond. A stable molecule then results. The rate law for iodine atom recombination in the presence of a foreign gas, e.g., argon, studied by flash photolysis is

$$\frac{d[I_2]}{dt} = k[I]^2[Ar] + k'[I]^2[I_2].$$

These two terms correspond to the two pathways

$$I + I + Ar \xrightarrow{k} I_2 + Ar$$

and

$$I + I + I_2 \xrightarrow{k'} I_2 + I_2.$$

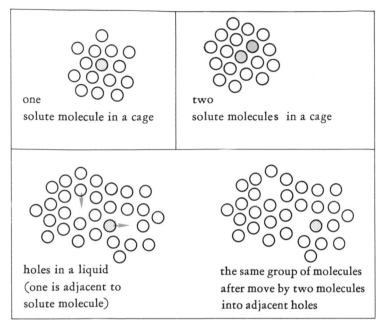

Figure 5–10. The structure of liquids and diffusion in liquids.

Since molecular iodine is necessarily present, it may act as a third body.

5–2. REACTIONS IN LIQUID SOLUTION

Molecules in liquids are in a constant state of motion. A particular molecule is in a cage made up of neighboring molecules. The thermal motion of molecules in the liquid state consists largely of molecules bouncing around within their cages. In a liquid there are some voids, spaces which are large enough to contain a molecule but which are empty. These voids are called "holes" in the liquid. When a molecule adjacent to a hole moves into the hole, both molecule and hole have moved. Diffusion in liquids consists of random motions of this type. Cages in liquids, holes in liquids, and the diffusion of molecules in liquids are pictured in Fig. 5–10.

Reactions in solution can occur no faster than reactant molecules can diffuse into the same solvent cage.[1] Just as the rates of most gas-phase reactions are much lower than the collision frequency, so also the rates of most reactions in solution are much lower than the frequency with which reactant molecules diffuse together. Failure of reaction to occur as rapidly as reactant molecules diffuse into each other's proximity is generally due to lack of requisite activation energy. During an *encounter*, the state in which reactant molecules are caged together, the bouncing of solvent molecules against the trapped reactants may provide activation energy for reaction to occur. If this does not happen, the encounter ends as reactant molecules escape from the same cage and diffuse away from one another; the encounter is fruitless. If, however, reactant molecules diffuse together with sufficient energy or if they acquire this energy from "rattling" against surrounding solvent molecules and reaction does occur, it is product molecules which diffuse away from the encounter. With techniques now available,[2] it is possible to study reactions which occur as rapidly as reactant molecules diffuse together. The value of the second-order rate constant for a diffusion-controlled reaction, as such reactions are called, depends upon the temperature, the nature of the reactant molecules, and the solvent. Such second-order rate constants are generally in the range 10^9 to 10^{10} liters/mole/sec. With the smaller of these values, a second-order reaction of B,

$$- \frac{d[B]}{dt} = k[B]^2,$$

with an initial concentration of B of 10^{-3} M is half over in 10^{-6} sec.

Second-order rate constants for reactions in solution are smaller than this if the probability of reaction during an encounter is low. The probability is low at ordinary temperatures if the activation energy is above 5 to 6 kcal *or* if some particularly improbable orientation of reactant partners is necessary for reaction to occur. The

---

[1] Possible exceptions are reactions which occur by electron transfer. If an oxidation-reduction reaction occurs by such a mechanism and if electron transfer can occur over a distance, it is possible that reaction can occur even though the reactants are not in the same cage. This question of the mechanism of electron-transfer reactions is not completely solved.

[2] Some of them will be discussed in Chap. 9.

or of the preceding sentence is important. There are reactions with low activation energies which nevertheless occur at rates much smaller than the rate of molecular encounters. From an examination of the rate constant expressed in the Arrhenius form

$$k = Ae^{-\Delta E_a/RT},$$

it is clear that a small rate constant may result from a small value of *A or* a large value of ΔE_a.

5–3. POTENTIAL-ENERGY CURVES
AND REACTION RATES

The motions of two or more atoms under the influence of their mutual attraction and repulsion conform to the law of conservation of energy. If an isolated system of atoms is considered, its energy content is constant. The relative amounts of kinetic energy and potential energy may vary, but the total energy of the group of atoms remains constant as long as the group of atoms is isolated.

Two hydrogen atoms, each with one electron, do not interact appreciably with one another if they are separated by a very large distance. As the separation is decreased, the atoms attract one another if the electrons have opposite spin but repel one another if the electrons have the same spin. For the pair of hydrogen atoms with electrons of the same spin, repulsion increases as the interatomic separation decreases; the potential energy of two such hydrogen atoms increases with this decrease. For the pair of hydrogen atoms with electrons of opposite spin, attraction increases as the interatomic separation decreases to 0.74×10^{-8} cm, but further decrease in the interatomic separation results in repulsion. Two hydrogen atoms with electrons of opposite spin repel one another strongly as the interatomic separation becomes appreciably less than 0.74×10^{-8} cm. The potential energy of two hydrogen atoms with electrons of opposite spin, therefore, first decreases and then increases as the interatomic separation decreases. The actual value of the potential energy of a pair of hydrogen atoms in some particular configuration depends upon the arbitrarily chosen zero of potential energy. The system of two hydrogen atoms is assigned zero poten-

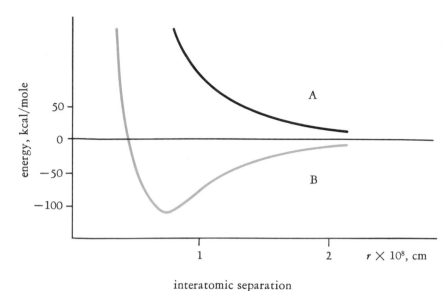

interatomic separation

Figure 5–11. The potential energy of two hydrogen atoms as a function of interatomic separation *r*. Curve A, the electrons have the same spin. Curve B, the electrons have opposite spin.

tial energy if the two atoms are separated by so large a distance that their interaction is infinitesimally small.

The potential energy of two hydrogen atoms as a function of interatomic separation is given in Fig. 5–11 for each situation, the electrons with the same spin (curve A) and with opposite spin (curve B). Points in the region of the graph above curve B correspond to two hydrogen atoms with the indicated separation having an amount of kinetic energy given by the distance of the point above the curve. Points below the zero of potential energy represent hydrogen atoms with insufficient kinetic energy to escape from one another. Such configurations correspond to molecular hydrogen with vibrational energy. (Actually, only certain definite amounts of vibrational energy are possible, a point to be discussed in Chap. 10. For the present this need not concern us.)

In Fig. 5–12, point *a* corresponds to two hydrogen atoms approach-

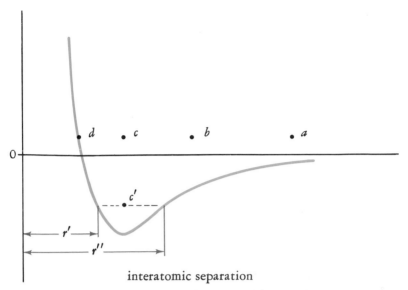

Figure 5–12. The potential energy of two hydrogen atoms with electrons of opposite spin. Points *a*, *b*, *c*, and *d* correspond to two hydrogen atoms with a constant amount of energy. The vertical distance from points *a*, *b*, and *c* to the curve gives the kinetic energy of the hydrogen atoms. Point *d* corresponds to hydrogen atoms with no kinetic energy, that is, only potential energy. Point *c'* corresponds to two hydrogen atoms in the form of a diatomic molecule. The kinetic energy of this configuration is the vibrational energy of the molecule. With this amount of energy, vibration causes the interatomic separation to vary between *r'* and *r"*.

ing one another for a head-on collision. With electrons of opposite spin, these atoms attract one another; at the separation corresponding to point *b*, their velocities are greater than they were at point *a*. The velocities corresponding to point *c* are greater still; but with further decrease of interatomic separation the velocities diminish, since at these values of interatomic separation the atoms repel one another. At a separation corresponding to point *d*, the kinetic energy of the hydrogen atoms is zero. The atoms are as close to each

other as is possible for two hydrogen atoms with this energy. In
this position the pair of atoms has more potential energy than corresponds to larger values of interatomic separation, so the atoms
repel one another. As the atoms move away from one another, potential energy is converted to kinetic energy. When the two hydrogen atoms are separated by distances corresponding to c, b, and a,
their total kinetic energy is the same as it was as they approached one
another at these distances. This is necessary, since energy is con-
served and nothing has happened in this collision to reduce the
energy of the pair of hydrogen atoms. Now, however, the atoms
are moving away from one another. This collision has not resulted
in formation of a molecule of hydrogen. But suppose another atom
is also involved in a collision of two hydrogen atoms. What is the
consequence if this atom bounces away from the pair of hydrogen
atoms with more kinetic energy than it brought into the collision?
The kinetic energy of the pair of hydrogen atoms is correspondingly
lowered; if it is lowered enough, e.g., to point c', the hydrogen
atoms are trapped by their mutual attraction and a hydrogen molecule results. This could not happen without the third body par-
ticipating in the collision. The analogous situation in iodine atom
recombination has already been discussed without using potential-
energy curves.

The value of a single coordinate, the interatomic separation r, is
all that is necessary to specify the potential energy of two hydrogen
atoms. The situation becomes more complex for a larger number
of atoms. For the case of four atoms, the situation corresponding to
one hydrogen molecule plus one iodine molecule, values of six
coordinates must be specified to define the potential energy of the
system. If the four atoms are numbered 1, 2, 3, and 4, the distances
which must be specified to define the relative positions of all four
atoms completely are r_{12}, r_{13}, r_{14}, r_{23}, r_{24}, and r_{34}, where r_{12} is the distance separating atoms 1 and 2, etc. Obviously we cannot make a
simple plot of potential energy vs. the values of all these coordinates;
it could not be pictured on the two-dimensional page of a book or
even as a three-dimensional relief map or the corresponding contour
map.

For this system and ones even more complicated, it is customary
to represent the potential energy as a function of a single parameter

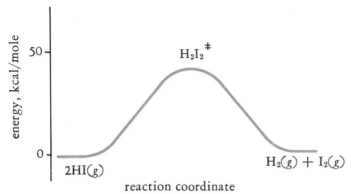

Figure 5–13. Potential energy as a function of reaction coordinate for the reaction $2HI = H_2 + I_2$.

called the *reaction coordinate*. For the bimolecular reaction of hydrogen and iodine, the reaction coordinate corresponds to the minimum-energy pathway already discussed. Figure 5–13 gives the potential energy vs. reaction coordinate for the hydrogen iodide-hydrogen iodine reaction. The vertical scale is the same as in Fig. 5–7; in Fig. 5–13 the curve is continuous, whereas in Fig. 5–7 the only quantities of significance are the vertical distances that correspond to energies. It is primarily the energies of the minima and the maximum in the continuous curve and corresponding values of interatomic distances which are important. It is the relative energy of the transition state and the initial state which determines the reaction rate.

PROBLEMS

1. (a) What is the average velocity of the gaseous molecules He, SO_2, and UF_6 at 400°K? (b) At what temperature do helium atoms have the same average velocity as sulfur dioxide molecules have at 400°K?   (*Ans.:* (b) 25°K)

2. At what temperature does the average kinetic energy of gaseous molecules equal the bond energy in I_2 (36 kcal/mole)? At what

temperature does the average kinetic energy of gaseous molecules equal the energy required to ionize the gaseous hydrogen atom (312 kcal/mole)?

3. If it is only the most energetic reactant molecules which react upon collision, do unreacted reactant molecules get colder and colder as the most energetic ones are used in the reaction? Explain.

4. The decomposition of nitrogen dioxide is a second-order reaction; in the absence of an inert gas, the rate law is

$$-\frac{d[NO_2]}{dt} = k_d[NO_2]^2$$

(a) At 592°K, the value of k_d is 4.98 × 10⁻¹ liter/mole/sec. What is the rate of decomposition of nitrogen dioxide at this temperature if the concentration of nitrogen dioxide is 0.0030 mole/liter? (b) Values of this rate constant at other temperatures are:

T (°K)	k_d, liter/mole/sec
603.5	0.775
627	1.81
651.5	4.11
656	4.74

What is the activation energy for this reaction?

(*Ans.:* $\Delta E_a = 27.2$ *kcal/mole*)

5. Explain the large difference in activation energy for decomposition of nitrogen dioxide at 600 to 650°K via the activated complex $\{NO_2 \cdot NO_2\}^{\ddagger}$ (27.2 kcal/mole) and at 1400 to 2300°K via the activated complex $\{NO_2 \cdot Ar\}^{\ddagger}$ (65.4 kcal/mole).

VI

Reaction Mechanisms

There is a relationship between concentration dependences of the rate of an *elementary reaction* and the balanced equation for the elementary reaction. Associated with the elementary reaction

$$2A \underset{k_2}{\overset{k_1}{\rightleftharpoons}} C + D$$

is the rate law

$$\frac{d[D]}{dt} = k_1[A]^2 - k_2[C][D],$$

in which the exponents are equal to the coefficients in the balanced equation for this one-step reaction. If the exponents in an experimental rate law are not equal to the coefficients in the balanced equation for the net reaction, the reaction must occur in a sequence of steps. If they are equal, the reaction *may* occur in a single step. This is a reasonable assumption if there is no contrary evidence and if the structures of reactants and products are compatible with reaction occurring in one elementary step. This is the situation for the principal pathway for the reaction

$$2HI = H_2 + I_2.$$

The experimental rate law

$$\frac{d[I_2]}{dt} = k_f[HI]^2 - k_r[H_2][I_2]$$

73

is consistent with reaction occurring in the elementary step

$$2HI \overset{k_f}{\underset{k_r}{\rightleftharpoons}} H_2 + I_2,$$

and the structures of reactants and products are also compatible with this.

6-1. INTERPRETATION OF RATE LAWS

The interpretation of rate laws for reactions which must consist of a sequence of elementary reactions is the problem usually facing the kineticist, since for most reactions the exponents in the rate law are not equal to the coefficients in the balanced equation. Some principles of chemical kinetics as well as the chemistry of diverse substances will now be illustrated by considering specific reactions.

Hypochlorite-Iodide Reaction

Here we shall discuss the meaning of inverse dependence of the reaction rate upon concentration. The rate law for the relatively rapid reaction of hypochlorite ion and iodide ion,

$$I^- + OCl^- = OI^- + Cl^-,$$

derived from experiments at a constant concentration of hydroxide ion (1.00 M) is

$$\frac{d[OI^-]}{dt} = k'[I^-][OCl^-].$$

One might assume that reaction occurs in a single step

$$I^- + OCl^- \rightarrow OI^- + Cl^-,$$

but this assumption is rendered untenable by the observation (made in experiments run at different concentrations of hydroxide ion) that k' depends upon hydroxide ion concentration. The more complete rate law

$$\frac{d[OI^-]}{dt} = \frac{k[I^-][OCl^-]}{[OH^-]}$$

involves the concentration of hydroxide ion in the denominator. It can be shown that this dependence of reaction rate upon hydroxide ion concentration results if hydroxide ion is produced in a rapidly established equilibrium prior to the rate-determining step. (Discussion of this rate law will help define the term "rate-determining step.") What reversible reaction involving hypochlorite ion and/or iodide ion as a reactant produces hydroxide ion? Since hypochlorous acid is a weak acid (K_{HOCl} = 3.4 × 10^{-8}), the reaction

$$OCl^- + H_2O \rightleftharpoons HOCl + OH^-$$

occurs to a slight extent, and it also satisfies the requirement of producing hydroxide ion. This reaction also produces hypochlorous acid. The rate of the over-all reaction will be inversely dependent upon the concentration of hydroxide ion if hypochlorous acid, the other product of this equilibrium, is a reactant in the rate-determining step. A reasonable slow step involving iodide ion and hypochlorous acid is

$$I^- + HOCl \rightarrow HOI + Cl^-,$$

in which chloride ion is displaced from hypochlorous acid by iodide ion. Although hypoiodous acid is a weak acid ($K_{HOI} \cong 10^{-11}$), iodine(I) is present in the reaction solutions ($[OH^-]$ = 0.25 to 1.00 M) predominantly as hypoiodite ion; this forms from hypoiodous acid in the rapid reaction

$$OH^- + HOI \rightleftharpoons H_2O + OI^-.$$

In summary, the experimental rate law is consistent with a reasonable three-step mechanism:

$$OCl^- + H_2O \rightleftharpoons HOCl + OH^- \qquad \text{rapid}$$
$$I^- + HOCl \rightarrow HOI + Cl^- \qquad \text{slow}$$
$$OH^- + HOI \rightleftharpoons H_2O + OI^- \qquad \text{rapid.}$$

The sum of the three steps is the over-all reaction

$$I^- + OCl^- = OI^- + Cl^-.$$

The second step is called the *rate-determining step* because the net reaction rate is equal to the forward rate of this step. In the sequence of three steps, this step is the first one the reverse of which does not lower the net reaction rate. It is for this reason that the forward rate at this step is equal to the net reaction rate.

Let us now prove that this postulated mechanism is consistent with the experimentally established rate law. Since conversion of hypoiodous acid to hypoiodite ion in the last step is both rapid and essentially complete, the rate of production of hypoiodite ion can be equated to the rate of the second step, which is rate-determining:

$$\frac{d[\text{OI}^-]}{dt} = k_2[\text{I}^-][\text{HOCl}],$$

where k_2 is the second-order rate constant for this bimolecular reaction. The concentration of hypochlorous acid is governed by equilibrium in the first reaction, and rearrangement of the equilibrium constant equation for this reaction gives

$$[\text{HOCl}] = K_1 \frac{[\text{OCl}^-]}{[\text{OH}^-]},$$

where K_1 is the equilibrium constant for the first reaction. (It may or may not be obvious that K_1 is equal to $K_{\text{H}_2\text{O}}/K_{\text{HOCl}} = (1.0 \times 10^{-14})/(3.4 \times 10^{-8}) = 2.9 \times 10^{-7}$; if this relationship is not obvious, convince yourself of its correctness.) Substitution of this expression for the concentration of hypochlorous acid into the rate law for the rate-determining step gives

$$\frac{d[\text{OI}^-]}{dt} = \frac{k_2 K_1 [\text{I}^-][\text{OCl}^-]}{[\text{OH}^-]},$$

a rate law with exactly the form of the experimental rate law. If this three-step sequence is, in fact, the mechanism, the empirical rate constant k is identified as the product $k_2 K_1$, that is,

$$k = k_2 K_1,$$

and the value of k_2 can be obtained:

$$k_2 = \frac{k}{K_1} = \frac{60 \text{ sec}^{-1}}{2.9 \times 10^{-7} \text{ mole/liter}}$$

$$= 2.1 \times 10^8 \text{ liter/mole/sec}.$$

It is interesting that this value is only 10- to 100-fold lower than the range of values expected for diffusion-controlled reactions.

Because of the correspondence between the experimental rate law and that derived from the proposed mechanism, this mechanism might be considered proved. *It is not;* the most one can say is that the mechanism is both reasonable and consistent with the kinetic data.

Kinetic data rarely if ever settle what happens after formation of the activated complex for the rate-determining step. The experimental rate law demonstrates that the activated complex contains one iodide ion *plus* one hypochlorite ion *plus* an undefined number of water molecules *minus* one hydroxide ion:

$$\{ICIOH(OH_2)_n{}^-\}^\ddagger.$$

Since the reaction order for water, the solvent, is not known, there is uncertainty with respect to the number of water molecules in the activated complex.

The mechanism already discussed implies a geometry

in which iodide ion attacks oxygen and displaces chloride ion. But perhaps iodide ion attacks chlorine

and displaces hydroxide ion, thereby producing the interhalogen compound iodine monochloride, which rapidly yields chloride ion and hypoiodite ion. This three-step mechanism

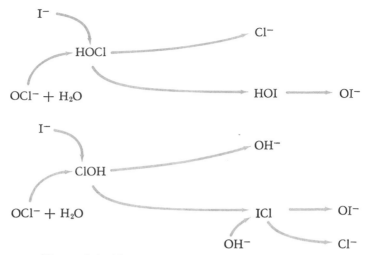

Figure 6–1. Alternate possible mechanisms for the reaction of iodide ion and hypochlorite ion.

$$OCl^- + H_2O \rightleftharpoons HOCl + OH^- \qquad \text{rapid}$$
$$I^- + HOCl \rightarrow ICl + OH^- \qquad \text{slow}$$
$$ICl + 2OH^- \rightarrow OI^- + Cl^- + H_2O \qquad \text{rapid}$$

is equally consistent with the experimentally determined rate law. In other words, an experimental rate law may be consistent with more than one mechanism. These two mechanisms consistent with the rate law for the hypochlorite-iodide reaction are pictured in Fig. 6–1.

Ammonium Cyanate-Urea Reaction

Here we shall discuss a reaction for which the structure of the activated complex is suggested by the structure of the product. Even if exponents in the experimental rate law are the same as coefficients in the balanced chemical equation, the reaction may not occur in a single elementary step involving the reactants in their predominant forms. An example is the reaction of ammonium ion and cyanate ion in aqueous solution to give urea; the net reaction is

$$NH_4^+ + OCN^- = OC(NH_2)_2.$$

This reaction is first order in ammonium ion and first order in cyanate ion, the experimental rate law being

$$\frac{d[OC(NH_2)_2]}{dt} = k[NH_4^+][OCN^-].$$

Because of the rapidly established equilibrium involving the Brönsted acid ammonium ion and the Brönsted base cyanate ion,

$$NH_4^+ + OCN^- \rightleftharpoons NH_3 + OCNH,$$

the product of concentrations $[NH_4^+][OCN^-]$ is directly proportional to the product of concentrations $[NH_3][OCNH]$. The equilibrium-constant equation for the acid-base reaction gives

$$[NH_3][OCNH] = K[NH_4^+][OCN^-].$$

Because of the structure of the product, a reaction of ammonium ion and cyanate ion makes less sense than one involving ammonia and isocyanic acid, which can be pictured as

The complete mechanism starting with ammonium ion and cyanate ion, the predominant reactant species, is assumed to be

$$NH_4^+ + OCN^- \overset{K}{\rightleftharpoons} NH_3 + OCNH \qquad \text{rapid}$$

$$NH_3 + OCNH \overset{k_2}{\longrightarrow} OC(NH_2)_2 \qquad \text{slow,}$$

with the second step rate-determining. The sum of these two reactions is the over-all reaction

$$NH_4^+ + OCN^- = OC(NH_2)_2,$$

and the rate law predicted by this mechanism is that observed:

$$\frac{d[OC(NH_2)_2]}{dt} = k_2[NH_3][OCNH].$$

But

$$[NH_3][OCNH] = K[NH_4^+][OCN^-]$$

and, therefore,

$$\frac{d[OC(NH_2)_2]}{dt} = k_2K[NH_4^+][OCN^-].$$

The empirical second-order rate constant is identified according to this mechanism as the product of the equilibrium constant for the rapid acid-base reaction and the rate constant for the rate-determining step involving ammonia and isocyanic acid.

Hydrogen Peroxide-Iodide Reaction

Consider now a reaction going by two pathways. The composition of activated complexes for the rate-determining steps are given by the concentration dependences of the rate law. This important principle can be further illustrated by considering the reaction of hydrogen peroxide and iodide ion in acidic solution:

$$H_2O_2 + 2H^+ + 3I^- = I_3^- + 2H_2O,$$

the rate law for which consists of two independent terms:

$$\frac{d[I_3^-]}{dt} = k[H_2O_2][I^-] + k\ [H_2O_2][H^+][I^-].$$

The reaction proceeds, therefore, by two independent pathways. The activated complex corresponding to the term which is first order in hydrogen peroxide and first order in iodide ion is made up of one hydrogen peroxide molecule and one iodide ion and has the composition $\{H_2O_2I^-\}^\ddagger$. The activated complex corresponding to the term that is first order in hydrogen peroxide, first order in hydrogen ion, and first order in iodide ion is made up of one hydrogen peroxide molecule, one hydrogen ion, and one iodide ion and has the composition $\{H_2O_2HI\}^\ddagger$.

Any detailed mechanisms proposed to explain these two rate law terms must have activated complexes of these compositions. Plausible mechanisms with these required features are the following:

path 1	$H_2O_2 + I^- \rightarrow OH^- + HOI$	slow
	$H^+ + OH^- \rightleftharpoons H_2O$	rapid
	$HOI + H^+ + 2I^- \rightleftharpoons I_3^- + H_2O$	rapid;
path 2	$H_2O_2 + I^- + H^+ \rightarrow H_2O + HOI$	slow
	$HOI + H^+ + 2I^- \rightleftharpoons I_3^- + H_2O$	rapid.

The first step given for each path is the rate-determining one. Following the slow step in each case are rapid reactions which complete the net chemical change.

Reaction orders higher than second do not demand reaction steps more complicated than bimolecular. Although the third-order term in the hydrogen peroxide-iodide rate law could arise from the rapid equilibrium

$$H^+ + I^- \rightleftharpoons HI$$

followed by the rate-determining step

$$HI + H_2O_2 \rightarrow H_2O + HOI,$$

it appears more likely to arise from the rapid equilibrium

$$H^+ + H_2O_2 \rightleftharpoons HOOH_2^+$$

followed by the rate-determining step

$$I^- + HOOH_2^+ \rightarrow H_2O + HOI.$$

In both cases the composition of the activated complex is $\{H_2O_2HI\}^\ddagger$, which is the composition demanded by the rate law. The rapidly established equilibria would be unfavorable in each case; both iodide ion and hydrogen peroxide are very weak Brönsted bases. The second of the two possible sequences of bimolecular steps seems more reasonable because the activated complex

yields products with a minimum of rearrangement. In this mechanism, displacement of water from the conjugate acid of hydrogen peroxide is accomplished by iodide ion.

Cerium(IV)–Chromium(III) Reaction

We shall consider here a stepwise oxidation-reduction reaction. Discussion of the rate of the iodide ion-hypochlorite ion reaction earlier in this chapter indicated the interpretation usually placed upon an inverse concentration dependence. The species which influences the rate inversely is produced in a rapidly established equilibrium prior to the rate-determining step. An interesting example of this kind of dependence is found in a reaction mentioned in Chap. 2, the oxidation of chromium(III) by cerium(IV) in sulfuric acid. In

solutions of constant concentration of sulfuric acid and varying concentrations of cerium(IV), cerium(III), chromium(III), and chro-
mium(VI), the experimental rate law is

$$-\frac{d[Ce^{IV}]}{dt} = \frac{k[Ce^{IV}]^2[Cr^{III}]}{[Ce^{III}]}$$

with an inverse dependence upon the concentration of cerium(III).
[In this example, correct formulas for species are not used; only the
oxidation state of each element is shown. This simplifies discussion,
since cerium(IV)—and possibly cerium(III) also—forms more than
one sulfate complex containing different numbers of sulfate ions.
Although chromium(III) also forms sulfate complexes, they form
slowly, and they do not participate in this reaction. These experiments at a constant concentration of sulfuric acid do not establish the
dependence of reaction rate upon concentrations of sulfate ion, hydrogen sulfate ion, and hydrogen ion.] The reaction

$$Ce^{IV} + Cr^{III} \rightleftarrows Ce^{III} + Cr^{IV}$$

producing chromium(IV), an unstable oxidation state, also produces
cerium(III), leading to an inverse dependence of the concentration of
chromium(IV) upon the concentration of cerium(III). If this reaction is followed by the rate-determining reaction of cerium(IV)
and unstable chromium(IV),

$$Ce^{IV} + Cr^{IV} \xrightarrow{k'} Ce^{III} + Cr^{V},$$

with the unstable chromium(V) reacting rapidly with another
cerium(IV),

$$Ce^{IV} + Cr^{V} \rightarrow Ce^{III} + Cr^{VI},$$

the observed rate law is the consequence. This can be shown by
first equating the rate of disappearance of cerium(IV) to 3 times the
rate of the rate-determining step. The factor 3 is needed because one
cerium(IV) ion is consumed in each of three successive steps. The
rate law is

$$-\frac{d[Ce^{IV}]}{dt} = 3k'[Ce^{IV}][Cr^{IV}],$$

where k' is the rate constant for the rate-determining step. But this rate law is not of much use, since it involves the concentration of an unstable intermediate, chromium(IV). The equilibrium concentration of this intermediate is established by the reversible reaction preceding the rate-determining step. From the equilibrium constant equation,

$$K = \frac{[\text{Ce}^{\text{III}}][\text{Cr}^{\text{IV}}]}{[\text{Ce}^{\text{IV}}][\text{Cr}^{\text{III}}]},$$

one can obtain

$$[\text{Cr}^{\text{IV}}] = K \frac{[\text{Ce}^{\text{IV}}][\text{Cr}^{\text{III}}]}{[\text{Ce}^{\text{III}}]}.$$

Substitution of this into the rate law for the rate-determining step gives:

$$-\frac{d[\text{Ce}^{\text{IV}}]}{dt} = 3k'K[\text{Ce}^{\text{IV}}] \frac{[\text{Ce}^{\text{IV}}][\text{Cr}^{\text{III}}]}{[\text{Ce}^{\text{III}}]},$$

which has the form of the experimentally established rate law. The rate constant of the empirical rate law is identified as $3k'K$ in this mechanism. As is generally true, the empirical rate law contributes no information regarding steps which follow the rate-determining step.

In Chap. 2 it was pointed out that kinetic data might provide information regarding intermediates along the reaction pathway. In the interpretation of the rate law just considered, the intermediate chromium(IV) is a participant in the reaction mechanism. It is doubtful if any other reasonable mechanism giving this rate law can be devised which does not involve a species of chromium(IV) as an intermediate.

Reactions That Are Zero Order in a Reactant

Even after being fully acquainted with the idea that reaction orders cannot be predicted from consideration of a balanced equation for the net reaction, one is startled to find a reaction rate uninfluenced by the concentration of one of the reactants. The explanation is simple enough: the reactant which does not influence the rate gets into the act after the rate-determining step.

Although hydrogen bonded to carbon is generally not very reactive, the inertness of saturated hydrocarbons being a consequence of this fact, the presence of such other groups as the carbonyl group, $\diagdown C = O$, makes certain hydrogen atoms more reactive. Hydrogen on a carbon atom adjacent to a carbonyl group can be readily replaced by halogen. An example is the iodination of acetone in aqueous solution. The net reaction for the formation of monoiodoacetone is[1]

$$I_2 + H\text{---}\overset{\overset{\displaystyle H}{|}}{\underset{\underset{\displaystyle H}{|}}{C}}\text{---}\overset{\overset{\displaystyle O}{\|}}{C}\text{---}\overset{\overset{\displaystyle H}{|}}{\underset{\underset{\displaystyle H}{|}}{C}}\text{---}H = I\text{---}\overset{\overset{\displaystyle H}{|}}{\underset{\underset{\displaystyle H}{|}}{C}}\text{---}\overset{\overset{\displaystyle O}{\|}}{C}\text{---}\overset{\overset{\displaystyle H}{|}}{\underset{\underset{\displaystyle H}{|}}{C}}\text{---}H + H^+ + I^-$$

The rate of disappearance of iodine in this reaction does not depend upon the concentration of iodine! In acidic solution it does, however, depend upon the concentration of hydrogen ion, which is a reaction product. A mechanism consistent with the rate law

$$-\frac{d[I_2]}{dt} = k[H_3O^+][(CH_3)_2CO]$$

is[2]

$$H\text{---}\overset{\overset{\displaystyle H}{|}}{\underset{\underset{\displaystyle H}{|}}{C}}\text{---}\overset{\overset{\displaystyle O}{\|}}{C}\text{---}\overset{\overset{\displaystyle H}{|}}{\underset{\underset{\displaystyle H}{|}}{C}}\text{---}H + H_3O^+ \rightleftharpoons H\text{---}\overset{\overset{\displaystyle H}{|}}{\underset{\underset{\displaystyle H}{|}}{C}}\text{---}\overset{\overset{\displaystyle \overset{\displaystyle H}{|}}{O^+}}{C}\text{---}\overset{\overset{\displaystyle H}{|}}{\underset{\underset{\displaystyle H}{|}}{C}}\text{---}H + H_2O \qquad \text{rapid}$$

acetone (keto form)

---

[1] Although further iodination of acetone proceeds in successive steps, these reactions occur more rapidly than the reaction forming monoiodoacetone.

[2] Hydrogen ion is represented as hydronium ion to show the role of water as a Brönsted base in this reaction mechanism. Water acts as a Brönsted base in the reverse of the first reaction step, in the rate-determining step, and in the step following the rate-determining step.

$$H_2O + H\text{—}\underset{\underset{H}{|}}{\overset{\overset{H}{|}}{C}}\text{—}\overset{\overset{O^+H}{\|}}{C}\text{—}\underset{\underset{H}{|}}{\overset{\overset{H}{|}}{C}}\text{—}H \rightarrow \underset{H}{\overset{H}{\diagdown}}C\text{=}\overset{\overset{OH}{|}}{C}\text{—}\underset{\underset{H}{|}}{\overset{\overset{H}{|}}{C}}\text{—}H + H_3O^+ \qquad \text{slow}$$

acetone (enol form)

$$H_2O + \underset{H}{\overset{H}{\diagdown}}C\text{=}\overset{\overset{OH}{|}}{C}\text{—}\underset{\underset{H}{|}}{\overset{\overset{H}{|}}{C}}\text{—}H + I_2 \rightarrow$$

$$I\text{—}\underset{\underset{H}{|}}{\overset{\overset{H}{|}}{C}}\text{—}\overset{\overset{O}{\|}}{C}\text{—}\underset{\underset{H}{|}}{\overset{\overset{H}{|}}{C}}\text{—}H + H_3O^+ + I^- \qquad \text{rapid}$$

Iodine reacts rapidly with the enol form of acetone after the enol is produced in the rate-determining step. The enol form of acetone is not present to an appreciable extent in solutions of acetone at equilibrium. This conversion of keto form to enol form goes by way of a protonated activated complex $\{(CH_3)_2C\text{=}\overset{+}{O}\text{—}H\}^{\ddagger}$, giving rise to the dependence of reaction rate upon the concentration of hydrogen ion. The fact that the bromine-acetone reaction has the same rate as the iodine-acetone reaction is additional evidence for slow formation of an intermediate which then rapidly reacts with iodine or bromine. The identity of the halogen does not influence the rate of its reaction with acetone because halogen participates after the rate-determining step.

6–2. INTERPRETATION OF REACTION STOICHIOMETRY

In many chemical systems, several reactions are possible. The products which actually form in a particular time interval are not the most stable ones if the relative reaction rates favor formation of a metastable system of products. Often, the nature of the products discloses significant information regarding reaction mechanism. For example, we learn about the existence of a common intermediate species in the reactions of certain alkyl halides from the fact that the corresponding chloride, bromide, and iodide give the same mixture of products. This information about the reaction mechanism is obtained from the observation that the products are not formed in the amounts that would be obtained at final chemical equilibrium. Nothing about reaction mechanism is disclosed by the observation that the reaction products correspond to the equilibrium state of the system. Regardless of the intermediate stages through which it may go, the system will come to its equilibrium state eventually; an examination of the system at that time tells nothing about the pathway by which the equilibrium state has been reached.

The Solvolysis of Tertiary Butyl Halides in Aqueous Ethanol

Alkyl halides, which are covalent substances, react in solution in several ways to give halide ion. In aqueous ethanol, tertiary butyl halides undergo the following reactions:

$$(CH_3)_3CX + H_2O = (CH_3)_3COH + H^+ + X^-$$
$$\text{\textit{tert}-butyl alcohol}$$

$$(CH_3)_3CX + C_2H_5OH = (CH_3)_3COC_2H_5 + H^+ + X^-$$
$$\text{ethyl \textit{tert}-butyl ether}$$

$$(CH_3)_3CX = (CH_3)_2C{=}CH_2 + H^+ + X^-$$
$$\text{isobutylene}$$

Tertiary butyl chloride, bromide, and iodide each react in a first-order reaction but react at very different rates; the fraction of reaction leading to the unsaturated product isobutylene is the same within experimental error (15 ± 2 per cent) for each halide. This is not the equilibrium proportion of isobutylene. (Presumably, the proportions of alcohol and ether are also the same from the different halides; this has been demonstrated in similar studies but not in the study being considered.) Since the relative amount of isobutylene is the same from each halide, it is reasonable to assume the same reaction intermediate is formed from the chloride, bromide, and iodide. Reactions of this common intermediate determine the yield of products. It would be a most unlikely coincidence if different species yielded the same nonequilibrium amounts of two products. If halide ion is lost by tertiary butyl halides, the residual species is tertiary butyl carbonium ion $(CH_3)_3C^+$. Presumably this is the unstable intermediate common to the reactions of the three tertiary butyl halides. The reactions in which tertiary butyl carbonium ion are formed are

$$(CH_3)_3CCl \rightarrow (CH_3)_3C^+ + Cl^-,$$
$$(CH_3)_3CBr \rightarrow (CH_3)_3C^+ + Br^-,$$

and

$$(CH_3)_3CI \rightarrow (CH_3)_3C^+ + I^-.$$

The rates would be expected to be different for the different halides since the chemical bond being broken is different in each reaction. The same carbonium ion is formed in each of these three ways; it can do three different things in water-ethanol solution:

$$(CH_3)_3C^+ + H_2O \rightarrow (CH_3)_3COH + H^+,$$
$$(CH_3)_3C^+ + C_2H_5OH \rightarrow (CH_3)_3COC_2H_5 + H^+,$$

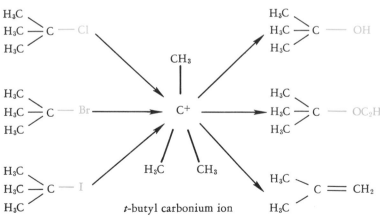

Figure 6-2. The mechanism of solvolysis of tertiary butyl halides in ethanol-water solutions.

or

$$(CH_3)_3C^+ \rightarrow (CH_3)_2C{=}CH_2 + H^+.$$

If the carbonium ion becomes completely separated from the halide ion with which it is associated before it undergoes one of these reactions, the relative rates of the three product-determining reactions will not depend upon which alkyl halide is parent of the tertiary butyl carbonium ion. The relative rates of the three product-determining reactions of tertiary butyl carbonium ion determine the relative yields of the three possible products, as illustrated in Fig. 6–2.

QUESTION:

What can be said about the first-order rate constants for the two reactions of an intermediate X,

$$X \xrightarrow{k_1} M$$

$$X \xrightarrow{k_2} N + P,$$

if the relative amounts of the products M and N formed are three parts of M per two parts of N?

Since both reactions are first order, the relative amounts of M and N will be directly proportional to the relative values of the two rate constants:

$$\frac{k_1}{k_2} = \frac{[M]}{[N]} = \frac{3}{2}.$$

Therefore

$$k_1 = \tfrac{3}{2}k_2.$$

On the average, of every five X's formed, three react to give M and two react to give N and P.

PROBLEMS

1. In this chapter, the rate law term

$$k'[H_2O_2][H^+][I^-]$$

was interpreted in terms of iodide ion displacing water from the conjugate acid of hydrogen peroxide ($HOOH_2^+$). Can you suggest an analogous mechanism corresponding to the rate law term

$$k[H_2O_2][I^-]?$$

2. Iodine slowly oxidizes hypophosphorous acid in aqueous solution. The equation for the net reaction is

$$H_3PO_2 + I_2 + H_2O = H_3PO_3 + 2H^+ + 2I^-,$$

and the rate law is

$$-\frac{d[H_3PO_2]}{dt} \cong k[H_3PO_2].$$

The rate is essentially independent of the concentration of iodine. How do you interpret this rate law?

3. Interpret in terms of a reaction mechanism the inverse dependence on hydrogen ion concentration in the rate law given in Prob. 1, Chap. 4.

VII

Reversible Reactions and Chemical Equilibrium

The net rate of a reversible reaction is the difference between the rate of the forward reaction and the rate of the reverse reaction:

net reaction rate = forward rate − reverse rate.

For the decomposition of hydrogen iodide,

$$2HI = H_2 + I_2,$$

an example already discussed, the rate law is

$$\frac{d[I_2]}{dt} = k_f[HI]^2 - k_r[H_2][I_2].$$

This rate law is an equation for the net reaction rate. The term $k_f[HI]^2$ gives the gross forward rate, and the term $k_r[H_2][I_2]$ gives the gross reverse rate. The former term gives approximately the net reaction rate in the early stage of an experiment before appreciable hydrogen and iodine have formed. The latter term gives approximately the net reaction rate in the early stage of an experiment with only hydrogen and iodine present initially. The net reaction rate under all conditions is the difference between these two terms as shown in Fig. 7–1.

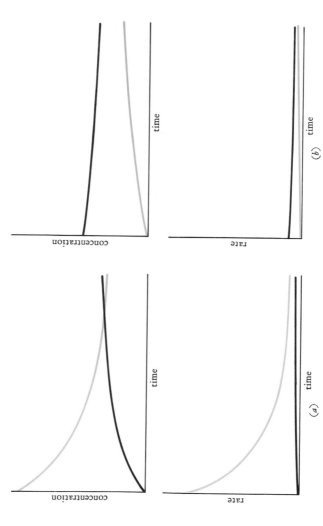

Figure 7–1. Concentrations and reaction rates in the reversible reaction $2HI \rightleftarrows H_2 + I_2$ (a) Starting with hydrogen iodide; (b) starting with hydrogen and iodine in equal amounts. The upper figures show concentration vs. time: hydrogen iodide, colored line; iodine, black line. The lower figures show values of the rate law terms: $k_f [HI]^2$, colored line; $k_r [H_2][I_2]$, black line. Notice in the upper figures that the concentration of hydrogen iodide approaches the same value in (a) and (b), and in the lower figures that $k_f [HI]^2$ and $k_r [H_2][I_2]$ approach one another at long times.

92

At chemical equilibrium the net reaction rate is zero; this is a consequence of equality of the gross forward rate and the gross reverse rate. For the example being considered, this gives

$$k_f[HI]^2 - k_r[H_2][I_2] = 0,$$

which can be rearranged to

$$\frac{k_f}{k_r} = \frac{[H_2][I_2]}{[HI]^2}.$$

The rate constants k_f and k_r have particular numerical values at a definite temperature, and, therefore, the quotient k_f/k_r also has a particular numerical value at a definite temperature. This equation is a mathematical relationship of concentrations of reactants and products at equilibrium.

The equilibrium constant equation

$$K = \frac{[H_2][I_2]}{[HI]^2}$$

is also a mathematical relationship of concentrations of reactants and products at equilibrium. The equilibrium constant equation and the equation derived from the rate law have the same form,

$$K = \frac{[H_2][I_2]}{[HI]^2} \qquad \frac{k_f}{k_r} = \frac{[H_2][I_2]}{[HI]^2} \, ,$$

and one can, therefore, equate the equilibrium constant and the ratio of the rate constants for the forward and reverse reactions. Since this pathway for hydrogen iodide decomposition is an elementary reaction, the example is deceptively simple. The principal conclusion is, however, valid for more complicated examples: *The equilibrium constant equation and the equation obtained by equating a positive rate law term and the corresponding negative rate law term are identical.*[1]

----

[1] This statement is not free of ambiguity, since a valid equilibrium constant equation may be obtained by raising the conventional equilibrium constant equation to some power, e.g., by squaring both sides of the equation to give

$$K' = K^2 = \frac{[H_2]^2[I_2]^2}{[HI]^4}.$$

We shall not concern ourselves with complexities introduced by this ambiguity.

We shall now consider a more complicated example. For the decomposition of nitrous acid in aqueous solution,

$$3HNO_2 = H^+ + NO_3^- + 2NO(g) + H_2O,$$

the rate law is

$$\frac{d[NO_3^-]}{dt} = \frac{k_f[HNO_2]^4}{P_{NO}^2} - k_r[H^+][NO_3^-][HNO_2],$$

where P_{NO} is the partial pressure of nitric oxide over the solution. If this rate is equated to zero, which is the condition of equilibrium, the resulting equation is

$$\frac{k_f[HNO_2]^4}{P_{NO}^2} - k_r[H^+][NO_3^-][HNO_2] = 0,$$

which can be rearranged to give

$$\frac{k_f}{k_r} = \frac{[H^+][NO_3^-]P_{NO}^2}{[HNO_2]^3}.$$

As in the simpler example, this has the same form as the equilibrium constant equation

$$K = \frac{[H^+][NO_3^-]P_{NO}^2}{[HNO_2]^3}.$$

Although neither the form of the positive term nor the form of the negative term could have been predicted from the balanced chemical equation, the function of concentrations resulting from equating the rate to zero is the same as the equilibrium constant expression.

A mechanism consistent with the rate law for this reversible reaction is

$$2HNO_2 \overset{K_1}{\rightleftharpoons} NO_2 + NO(g) + H_2O \qquad \text{rapid}$$

$$2NO_2 \overset{K_2}{\rightleftharpoons} N_2O_4 \qquad \text{rapid}$$

$$N_2O_4 + H_2O \overset{k_3}{\underset{k_{-3}}{\rightleftharpoons}} H^+ + NO_3^- + HNO_2 \qquad \text{rate-determining}$$

Consideration of the reverse reaction is simpler and will be given first. If the third reaction is rate-determining, the reverse rate according to this mechanism is

$$-\frac{d[\mathrm{NO_3^-}]}{dt} = k_{-3}[\mathrm{H^+}][\mathrm{NO_3^-}][\mathrm{HNO_2}],$$

which is that observed; therefore, we identify k_r as k_{-3}. The same reaction step is rate-determining for both forward and reverse reactions, and the rate for the forward reaction according to this mechanism is

$$\frac{d[\mathrm{NO_3^-}]}{dt} = k_3[\mathrm{N_2O_4}].$$

(Since water is the solvent and is present at essentially constant concentration in all solutions, its concentration is not shown in the rate law.) This rate law involves dinitrogen tetroxide, a species present at a low concentration dictated by equilibria represented in the first and second reactions. The concentration of dinitrogen tetroxide is related to concentrations of species present in large amounts (i.e., $\mathrm{H^+}$, $\mathrm{NO_3^-}$, $\mathrm{HNO_2}$, and NO) by

$$[\mathrm{N_2O_4}] = K_2[\mathrm{NO_2}]^2;$$

but

$$[\mathrm{NO_2}] = K_1\frac{[\mathrm{HNO_2}]^2}{P_\mathrm{NO}},$$

and, therefore,

$$[\mathrm{N_2O_4}] = K_1^2K_2\frac{[\mathrm{HNO_2}]^4}{P_\mathrm{NO}^2}.$$

The rate of the forward reaction is, therefore,

$$\frac{d[\mathrm{NO_3^-}]}{dt} = k_3K_1^2K_2\frac{[\mathrm{HNO_2}]^4}{P_\mathrm{NO}^2},$$

which has the form of the experimentally observed rate law for the forward reaction. The rate constant k_f of the experimental rate law is identified, therefore, as the product $k_3K_1^2K_2$.

The single positive term and the single negative term in this rate law pertain to the same reaction pathway, and the composition of the activated complex corresponding to the positive term is the same as that corresponding to the negative term. The composition of activated complex deduced from the positive term $k_f[\mathrm{HNO_2}]^4/P_\mathrm{NO}^2$ is

$$4(\mathrm{HNO_2}) - 2(\mathrm{NO}) \pm n(\mathrm{H_2O}) = \{\mathrm{H_4N_2O_6} \pm n\mathrm{H_2O}\}^\ddagger,$$

and that from the negative term $k_r[\text{H}^+][\text{NO}_3^-][\text{HNO}_2]$ is

$$(\text{H}^+) + (\text{NO}_3^-) + (\text{HNO}_2) \pm m(\text{H}_2\text{O}) = \{\text{H}_2\text{N}_2\text{O}_5 \pm m\text{H}_2\text{O}\}^\ddagger.$$

The composition with respect to hydrogen and oxygen is uncertain because of the impossibility of obtaining the order of reaction with respect to the solvent. For $m - n = 1$, the compositions deduced from each term are the same. In the mechanism given above, the value of m is 0 and the value of n is -1.

We have already learned that more than one pathway may contribute appreciably to the reaction rate. Since each pathway is necessarily a pathway for both forward and reverse reaction, there are as many negative terms in the complete rate law as there are positive terms. Each negative term corresponds to one positive term, and the pair of terms together corresponds to one reaction pathway.

PROBLEMS

1. The rate law for reaction of chromium(III) ion and thiocyanate ion has been given in Prob. 1, Chap. 4. This reaction is reversible. What is a possible form of the rate law for the reverse reaction? What statement can you make regarding the rates of forward and reverse reactions by each of the three pathways at chemical equilibrium?

2. The reaction of triiodide ion and arsenious acid,

$$\text{H}_3\text{AsO}_3 + \text{I}_3^- + \text{H}_2\text{O} = \text{H}_3\text{AsO}_4 + 3\text{I}^- + 2\text{H}^+,$$

is reversible. At a great distance from equilibrium, the rate of the forward reaction is

$$- \frac{d[\text{I}_3^-]}{dt} = k\,\frac{[\text{H}_3\text{AsO}_3][\text{I}_3^-]}{[\text{H}^+][\text{I}^-]^2}.$$

What is a possible form of the rate law for the reverse reaction?

3. In this chapter it was stated that the same reaction step is rate-determining for both the forward and reverse reaction. Rationalize this in terms of a potential-energy diagram (see Chap. 5) for a multistep reaction pathway.

VIII

Catalysis

The rate of a reaction may be increased by a substance not appearing in the balanced equation for the net reaction. Such a substance is called a *catalyst*, and the phenomenon is called *catalysis*. Some examples of catalysis are very dramatic. Reactions which occur at a negligible rate in the absence of a catalyst may, in the presence of a proper catalyst, be employed on a large scale in industry. The octane rating of gasoline is raised by converting straight-chain hydrocarbons to branched isomers, e.g.,

$$
\begin{array}{ccccc}
\text{H} & \text{H} & \text{H} & \text{H} \\
| & | & | & | \\
\text{H--C--C--C--C--H} & = \\
| & | & | & | \\
\text{H} & \text{H} & \text{H} & \text{H}
\end{array}
$$

normal butane   isobutane

This isomerization reaction is catalyzed by aluminum chloride.

Substances which initiate chain reactions satisfy in a general way the definition of a catalyst. Although the initiator may be altered

97

chemically, an enormous amount of chain reaction occurs with the consumption of only a trace of initiator.

Since a catalyst does not appear in the balanced equation for the net reaction, its concentration does not appear in the equilibrium constant equation. A substance acting as a catalyst for a forward reaction will, therefore, also act as a catalyst for the reverse reaction. Corresponding positive and negative terms in a rate law couple to give an equilibrium constant equation which does not contain the concentration of a catalyst. If the concentration of a catalyst is present as a factor in a positive term of the rate law, it must also be present as a factor in the corresponding negative term. Although a catalyst cannot make a reaction occur to an extent greater than corresponds to equilibrium, it can greatly increase the rate at which equilibrium is attained.

We have already seen that a reaction may proceed by more than one pathway. A catalyst furnishes one or more additional pathways which allow the reaction to occur more rapidly.

The types of catalysis discussed in this chapter include catalysis by compensating reactions, catalysis by enzymes, catalysis by surfaces, and the initiation of free-radical polymerization. In each case, the catalyst (or initiator) opens new reaction pathways.

If an added substance makes possible a new pathway along which the rate of reaction is low relative to other existing pathways, the reaction simply ignores this new pathway and goes via the other pathways. For every reaction there are probably a large number of pathways which are energetically unfavorable; generally these will not be detected.

8–1. CATALYSIS BY COMPENSATING REACTIONS

Some cases of catalysis involve a pair of compensating reactions which interconvert the catalyst between two forms. The catalyst does not, therefore, suffer any net change as a result of compensating reactions. Catalysis of decomposition of hydrogen peroxide in acidic aqueous solution by bromine and bromide ion is an example of this type of catalysis. The reaction

$$2H_2O_2 = 2H_2O + O_2(g)$$

is one with an enormous tendency to occur but one which occurs very, very slowly in pure solutions. The enormous tendency for reaction to occur can be put in quantitative terms:

$$K = \frac{P_{O_2}}{[H_2O_2]^2} = 10^{37} \text{ atm-liter}^2/\text{mole}^2.$$

A hypothetical pressure of oxygen of 10^{37} atm is required to cause the reverse reaction to build up an equilibrium concentration of hydrogen peroxide of one molar. Catalysis of this reaction by bromine and bromide ion in acidic solution is well understood. Hydrogen peroxide is capable of acting both as oxidizing agent and reducing agent, and each of the two reactions

$$Br_2 + H_2O_2 = 2Br^- + 2H^+ + O_2(g)$$

$$2Br^- + H_2O_2 + 2H^+ = Br_2 + 2H_2O$$

can occur as an independent reaction. The sum of these two reactions is

$$2H_2O_2 = 2H_2O + O_2(g).$$

This is the only net chemical change which occurs when the compensating reactions proceed at the same rate. Under these circumstances, decomposition of hydrogen peroxide is catalyzed by the bromine–bromide ion couple. The compensating reactions depicted in Fig. 8–1 are not the forward and reverse of one another. When these two reactions occur at the same rate, a steady state in which

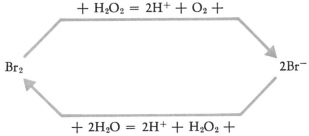

Figure 8–1. Compensating reactions which result in decomposition of hydrogen peroxide.

the concentrations of bromine and bromide ion do not change is established. This is not the consequence of an equilibrium, which results if a reaction and *its reverse* occur at the same rate. The compensating reactions creating the steady state are not the forward and reverse of the same reaction.

This kind of pathway for catalysis of the decomposition of hydrogen peroxide is open to many oxidation-reduction couples. Examination of the half-reactions[1]

$$H_2O_2 = O_2(g) + 2H^+ + 2e^- \qquad E^\circ = -0.68 \text{ volt}$$

$$2H_2O = H_2O_2 + 2H^+ + 2e^- \qquad E^\circ = -1.77 \text{ volts}$$

indicates that any couple involving an oxidized form O and a reduced form R,

$$R = O + ne^- \qquad -1.77 < E^\circ < -0.68,$$

with an oxidation potential approximately in the range shown is a couple capable of acting in this way. The reduced form R can reduce hydrogen peroxide, and the oxidized form O can oxidize hydrogen peroxide. The bromine-bromide couple satisfies the criterion

$$2Br^- = Br_2 + 2e^- \qquad E^\circ = -1.07 \text{ volts.}$$

Whether a couple that satisfies this criterion acts as a catalyst in this way cannot be answered simply by examining values of oxidation potentials. The relative rates of possible competing reactions are relevant, and these cannot be predicted from consideration of oxidation potentials. There are many different catalysts for decomposition of hydrogen peroxide, and all do not necessarily act through a mechanism of the sort shown to be responsible for catalysis by the bromine-bromide couple.

8–2. ENZYME CATALYSIS

Many chemical changes occurring in living systems are catalyzed by enzymes. These very efficient catalysts are proteins of high molecular weight, and the catalytic properties are believed to reside

---

[1] The sign convention used here corresponds to the oxidized form of a couple being a better oxidizing agent the more negative the value of E°.

in particular regions of the molecule called "active sites." Some enzymes are very efficient catalysts for only a single reaction; they show no catalytic properties for other reactions.

One big puzzle is the role of the protein structure in determining the specificity of enzymes. Urease, an enzyme of molecular weight 480,000, is a specific catalyst for conversion of urea to ammonium ion and bicarbonate ion in acidic solution:

$$CO(NH_2)_2 + H^+ + 2H_2O = 2NH_4^+ + HCO_3^-.$$

Fumarase, an enzyme of molecular weight 220,000, is a specific catalyst for the reversible hydration of fumarate ion to *l*-malate ion

fumarate ion   *l*-malate ion

Urease does not catalyze conversion of fumarate ion to *l*-malate ion, and fumarase does not catalyze conversion of urea to ammonium ion and bicarbonate ion.

Fumarase catalyzes formation of only one of the two possible optical isomers of malate ion.[1] The active site in fumarase must, therefore, be asymmetric and have the appropriate geometry for *l*-malate ion but not for its mirror image. The uncatalyzed reaction, on the other hand, gives equal amounts of the two optical isomers.

Figure 8–2 illustrates the way in which the active site of an enzyme may fulfill its specific task.

Although an oversimplification, some important features of enzyme catalysis can be discussed with reference to a reaction

$$S = P$$

which, in the presence of enzyme, goes by a pathway of two successive reactions:

---

[1] Since malate ion contains a carbon atom to which four different groups are attached, it is asymmetric. Malate ion, therefore, exists in two isomeric forms which are mirror images of one another. One of these is called the *d* form and the other is called the *l* form.

uncatalyzed reaction:

enzyme-catalyzed reaction:

1. substrate diffuses   2. enzyme-substrate   3. products diffuse from
     to active site   complex   active site

Figure 8–2. An enzyme-catalyzed reaction. In the enzyme-substrate complex, the dissociation of substrate occurs more readily than in the uncatalyzed reaction. Presumably this is due to interaction between the substrate and the "active site."

$$S + E \rightleftharpoons ES$$
$$ES \rightleftharpoons E + P$$

in which S, E, ES, and P represent substrate (that is, the reactant), enzyme, a complex of enzyme and substrate, and product, respectively. This mechanism for enzyme-catalyzed reactions is called the Michaelis-Menten mechanism, after the investigators who first proposed it in 1913. This mechanism is suggested by the reaction order with respect to substrate at constant total enzyme concentration. At low substrate concentration the reaction is first order in substrate, and at high substrate concentration the reaction is zero order in substrate. This is shown in Fig. 8–3. At low substrate concentration the reaction rate is directly proportional to the substrate

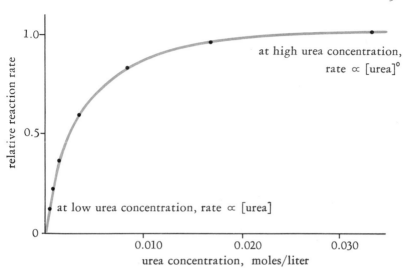

Figure 8–3. The rate of hydrolysis of urea catalyzed
by urease. The enzyme concentration is the same in all
experiments. [Data from the work of G. B. Kistiakowsky
and A. J. Rosenberg, *J. Am. Chem. Soc.*, **74**, 502
(1952).]

concentration. At high substrate concentration the reaction rate
reaches a limiting value, and a further increase in substrate concentration does not increase the rate. This behavior is consistent with
the two-step mechanism. The predominant form of enzyme is E
at low substrate concentration, and the concentration of the enzyme-
substrate complex increases directly in proportion to substrate concentration. The predominant form of the enzyme is ES, the enzyme-
substrate complex, at high substrate concentration, and further
increase of the concentration of substrate cannot increase the concentration of enzyme-substrate complex. That is, essentially all
active sites on the enzyme molecules are occupied by substrate
molecules. According to this mechanism the product is formed by
decomposition of enzyme-substrate complex, and the rate of formation of product will depend, therefore, upon the concentration of
this species.

For the urease-catalyzed decomposition of urea, the half-time for the first-order reaction

$$ES \rightarrow P + E$$

is $\sim 10^{-4}$ sec at 25°C. For the uncatalyzed reaction

$$S \rightarrow P,$$

the half-time is $\sim 10^9$ sec at 25°C. (This value is extrapolated from measurements made at higher temperatures.) This enormous factor of $\sim 10^{13}$ suggests that something rather dramatic is done to urea in the enzyme-substrate complex to make it decompose so much more rapidly than it does in the absence of enzyme. In actual experiments, reaction via the enzyme-catalyzed pathway is not, however, 10^{13}-fold faster than the uncatalyzed reaction, since under the experimental conditions,

$$\{[E] + [ES]\} \ll [S],$$

only a very small fraction of the substrate is tied up in the form of the reactive enzyme-substrate complex at any particular time.

It is an oversimplification to attribute all catalysis to it, but lowering of the activation energy is certainly a factor in the decomposition of urea. The uncatalyzed and urease-catalyzed reactions have activation energies of 32.7 and 8.85 kcal/mole, respectively. (The latter activation energy is that associated with the first-order rate constant for the reaction $ES \rightarrow E + P$.)

8–3. HETEROGENEOUS CATALYSIS

Many industrially important reactions of gaseous substances are catalyzed by surfaces. Among these reactions are the Haber synthesis of ammonia from hydrogen and nitrogen catalyzed by iron and other transition metals, the contact process for oxidation of sulfur dioxide to sulfur trioxide catalyzed by vanadium oxides or metallic platinum, and isomerization of normal butane to isobutane,

$$CH_3CH_2CH_2CH_3 = (CH_3)_3CH$$

already mentioned in the introduction to this chapter.

The dependence of the rate of many of these catalyzed reactions upon the pressure of the gaseous reactant resembles the dependence of reaction rate upon substrate concentration given in Fig. 8–3. That is, the rate is directly proportional to the pressure of the gas at low pressures and relatively independent of the pressure of the gas at high pressures. This experimentally observed dependence is consistent with a mechanism involving adsorption of the gaseous reactant onto the surface where it reacts with the other reactant, as depicted in Fig. 8–4. At low pressures of gas only a small fraction of the surface is covered, and the extent of coverage is proportional to the pressure; at high pressures the catalyst surface is completely "saturated," and further increase in pressure does not increase the amount of adsorbed gaseous reactant. The rate of reaction is not,

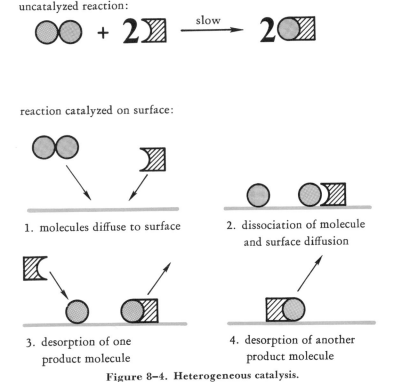

Figure 8–4. Heterogeneous catalysis.

therefore, increased further by increasing the pressure of the gaseous reactant.

This formal description of the dependence of reaction rate upon pressure of gaseous reactant leaves completely unanswered the question of why the adsorbed reactant is so much more reactive. A clue to the answer is the evolution of a large amount of heat, 30 to 100 kcal/mole, accompanying adsorption of gaseous reactant by catalyst for some systems. This suggests a real chemical combination between catalyst and gaseous reactant, and it leads to naming this adsorption process "chemisorption." The combination of catalyst and reactant must not, however, be so strong that the reactant does not react further to give the product.

In catalysis of reactions of hydrogen by metal surfaces, there is evidence that the hydrogen molecule is dissociated to monatomic units when chemisorbed. The data do not allow one to decide whether the monatomic units are hydrogen atoms or hydride ions (H^-). If the monatomic units are hydride ions, some metal ions must be formed in the metallic catalyst since the electrons which convert molecular hydrogen to hydride ion come from the metallic catalyst. The metal hydride can be viewed as a reaction intermediate in much the same way as the enzyme-substrate complex is a reaction intermediate in enzyme-catalyzed reactions. Definite hydride compounds are known for some metals which are efficient hydrogenation catalysts (e.g., palladium). The electronic structure of the metal is certainly relevant, and it is interesting that certain metal ions act as catalysts for reactions of molecular hydrogen in aqueous solution, these metal ions $(Cu^{2+}, Cu^+, Pd^{2+}, Ag^+,$ and $Hg^{2+})$ being isoelectronic with neutral atoms of metals (Co, Ni, Ru, Pd, and Pt), which are efficient heterogeneous catalysts.

The complete mechanism of catalysis by surfaces must involve several steps. For this reason the subject is really more complicated than the present discussion suggests. The gaseous molecules diffuse to the surface; they are adsorbed by the surface; they react; and then the product(s) desorb from the surface and diffuse away. It is not simple to unscramble information about each of these steps from observations of the rate of reaction as a function of the pressure(s) of gaseous reactant(s) and the temperature. Much progress is, however, being made in this area.

8-4. INITIATION OF FREE-RADICAL POLYMERIZATION

The initiator of a chain reaction is essentially a catalyst. Although it is altered in the reaction, a small amount of the appropriate initiator can cause a large amount of reaction to occur. The situation, therefore, approaches that of "true" catalysis, where an infinite amount of chemical reaction can result from action of a small amount of catalyst.

Ethylene (CH_2CH_2) and substituted ethylenes (CH_2CHX) polymerize under appropriate conditions to form materials of high molecular weight. The net reaction for polymerization of a substituted ethylene can be represented by

$$n \quad \begin{matrix} H & & H \\ \diagdown & & \diagup \\ & C = C & \\ \diagup & & \diagdown \\ H & & X \end{matrix} \quad = \quad \left(\begin{matrix} H & & H \\ | & & | \\ -C & - & C- \\ | & & | \\ H & & X \end{matrix} \right)_n$$

The rate of the uncatalyzed reaction is, however, generally low. Reactions of this type can be initiated by the action of substances which generate free radicals. Benzoyl peroxide is such a substance. It, like many organic peroxides, is unstable and decomposes to give benzoyl radicals ($C_6H_5CO_2 \cdot$),

$$\underset{\displaystyle C_6H_5C}{\overset{\displaystyle O}{\overset{\|}{}}} - O - O - \underset{\displaystyle CC_6H_5}{\overset{\displaystyle O}{\overset{\|}{}}} \rightarrow 2 \underset{\displaystyle C_6H_5CO \cdot}{\overset{\displaystyle O}{\overset{\|}{}}}$$

these may decompose further to give phenyl radicals ($C_6H_5 \cdot$)

$$\underset{\displaystyle C_6H_5CO \cdot}{\overset{\displaystyle O}{\overset{\|}{}}} \rightarrow C_6H_5 \cdot + CO_2$$

Either of these free radicals can react with ethylene or a substituted ethylene to start a sequence of propagation reactions:

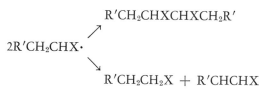

$$R(CH_2CHX)_n\cdot + CH_2CHX \rightarrow R(CH_2CHX)\cdot_{n+1},$$

in which $R\cdot$ represents the free radical that initiates the chain. The polymer grows with each successive bimolecular reaction, the product in each step being a radical which can react with a monomer molecule to lengthen the polymer. Polymerization generally terminates in a reaction of two growing radicals

$$
\begin{array}{c}
\nearrow \quad R'CH_2CHXCHXCH_2R' \\
2R'CH_2CHX\cdot \\
\searrow \quad R'CH_2CH_2X + R'CHCHX
\end{array}
$$

In neither of these reactions are the products radicals, and, therefore, the sequence of reactions has terminated. The length of the polymer depends upon the number of chain-propagation steps which occur before chain termination stops the polymer from growing. Polymers built up of 10^3 or more monomers can be formed in the type of reaction under consideration. A relatively small amount of initiator can, therefore, cause polymerization of a large amount of monomer.

PROBLEMS

1. The dependence upon substrate concentration of the rate of many enzyme-catalyzed reactions resembles that shown in Fig. 8–3.

An equation which fits this sort of data taken at constant enzyme concentration is

$$\text{rate} = \frac{k[S]}{K + [S]}.$$

(a) Explain how this equation is consistent with the statements made in Chap. 8: the reaction is first order in substrate at low substrate concentration and zero order in substrate at high substrate concentration. (b) Rearrange this equation to a linear form $(y = mx + b)$. (c) The data plotted in Fig. 8–3 are:

Urea, mole/liter	Rate, mole/liter/sec
0.00032	0.130
0.00065	0.226
0.00129	0.362
0.00327	0.600
0.00830	0.846
0.0167	0.975
0.0333	1.03

Plot these data according to the linear equation derived in part (b). Obtain values of k and K from the slope and intercept of this straight line.

(*Ans.: $k = 1.12$ mole/liter/sec; $K = 2.64 \times 10^{-3}$ mole/liter*)

2. Styrene

is a substituted ethylene which polymerizes in the way described in this chapter. Draw the structure of a segment of a polystyrene polymer. Is there more than one possible structure?

3. Describe a perpetual motion machine that would be possible if one particular catalyst catalyzed the reaction

$$N_2 + 3H_2 = 2NH_3$$

and not its reverse, and another particular catalyst catalyzed the reaction

$$2NH_3 = N_2 + 3H_2$$

and not its reverse.

IX

The Study of Very Fast Reactions

Conventional methods for study of reaction kinetics cannot be applied to reactions which go to equilibrium in a few seconds or less. At one time such reactions were too fast for kinetic study, but that is no longer true.

9–1. FLOW METHODS

A reaction cannot be studied under definite concentration conditions if most of the reaction occurs while the reactants are being mixed. Similarly, only an inappreciable amount of reaction should occur during the time required to make an observation of the extent of reaction. Fortunately, there are procedures for overcoming each of these limitations, and reactions which go to completion in even a millisecond (10^{-3} sec) can now be studied by using flow methods.

Solutions flowing through two tubes into a mixing chamber of appropriate design can be thoroughly mixed in times as short as 10^{-3} sec. The mixed solution then flows into an observation tube. With flow of completely mixed solution at a constant rate, reaction occurs to a particular extent at each position along the observation tube. This condition prevails because each position along the observation tube corresponds, for a particular flow rate, to the lapse of some definite time interval after mixing. In this arrangement, the observation need not involve equipment with fast response, since with a constant flow rate the concentrations at a particular point along the observation tube do not change. It is possible to make observations as soon as a few milliseconds after mixing. A schematic diagram of this type of experimental equipment is given in Fig. 9–1.

Measurement of light absorption may be used conveniently in this type of experiment to determine the extent of reaction if the absorp-

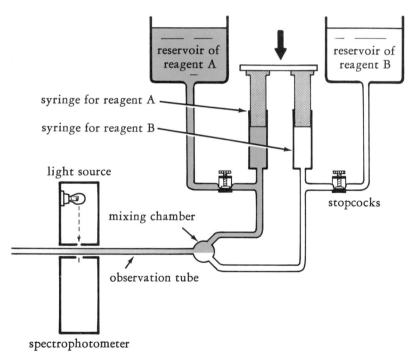

Figure 9–1. Schematic diagram of equipment for rapidly mixing reactants and observing the transmission of light by the reaction mixture a few milliseconds after mixing. Pistons in the two syringes are linked together as shown so they can be driven at the same rate.

tion spectrum of the product differs from that of the reactant. The spectrophotometric equipment can be set up with the beam of light passing through the solution at a point "downstream" from the point of mixing. If experiments are performed with different rates of flow, values of light absorption at this one particular point provide data from which a plot of extent of reaction vs. time can be prepared. With observation points at several positions, the same data can be accumulated at one particular flow rate.

Among rapid reactions which have been studied in this way is the reversible combination of oxygen and hemoglobin, the oxygen-carrying substance of blood. This complicated molecule will be represented as Hb. The deoxygenation

$$HbO_2 \rightarrow Hb + O_2$$

can be conveniently studied by mixing solutions of oxyhemoglobin, represented as HbO_2, with hyposulfite ion $S_2O_4{}^{2-}$. Hyposulfite ion reacts very, very rapidly with oxygen but does not react directly with oxyhemoglobin; the over-all change in the hyposulfite-oxygen reaction is

$$H_2O + S_2O_4{}^{2-} + O_2 = HSO_3{}^- + SO_4{}^{2-} + H^+.$$

The dissociation of oxyhemoglobin can be studied, therefore, as an irreversible change. Each oxygen molecule given up by oxyhemoglobin is "gobbled up" by hyposulfite before it has a chance to recombine with hemoglobin. At pH = 7.0 and 20°C, this dissociation reaction has a half-time of 0.015 sec, determined from the decrease in light absorption accompanying dissociation of red oxyhemoglobin. There is much interest in the rate of this reaction because of its obvious relevance in oxygen transport.

Although spectrophotometric observation of extent of reaction is widely used in flow methods of studying fast reactions, other methods are possible. One is the measurement of temperature at various positions along the observation tube by means of an appropriately designed probe containing a thermocouple. The heat absorbed or evolved with occurrence of reaction causes the temperature of the flowing solution to fall or rise. Because of the high rate of flow of solution, negligible heat is exchanged between the flowing solution and its surroundings, and the temperature change of the solution at a particular point along the observation tube is a measure of the amount of reaction which has occurred at that point, as illustrated in Fig. 9–2. A reaction studied in this way is[1]

$$CO_2(aq) + OH^- = HOCO_2^-.$$

With 0.0074 M carbon dioxide and 0.04 M hydroxide ion at 20°C, the reaction goes halfway to completion in 0.0054 sec. In this particular experiment the total temperature rise corresponding to complete reaction is 0.076°; this small temperature rise, although conveniently measurable, does not change the reaction velocity appreciably.

9–2. RELAXATION METHODS

Many reactions occur too rapidly to be amenable to any kinetic procedure involving mixing of reactant solutions, even by the flow procedure just described. Some very fast reactions can be studied by a relaxation method, in which a system at chemical equilibrium is disturbed by a sudden alteration of temperature or pressure. A sudden alteration in pressure can be accomplished by bursting the diaphragm of a high-pressure chamber surrounding the reaction vessel (Fig. 9–3). The pressure can be made to decrease by 100 atm within ~10^{-3} sec. A sudden increase in temperature can be accomplished by passage of an electric current for a very short interval of time. The discharge of a capacitor provides such a short-duration pulse of current. Observations made in a region between the electrodes will not be disturbed by the chemical change which occurs at the electrodes during the discharge. By this means, a temperature increase of 10° can be obtained in 10^{-5} sec.

The position of equilibrium depends upon the temperature if heat is evolved or absorbed in the reaction, and it depends upon the pressure if the volume of the system changes with occurrence of reaction. The new position of equilibrium, corresponding to the new tempera-

---

[1] Carbon dioxide in aqueous solution is present predominantly as CO_2, less than 1 per cent being present as H_2CO_3. The reaction of H_2CO_3 with hydroxide ion is very much faster than the reaction being considered here.

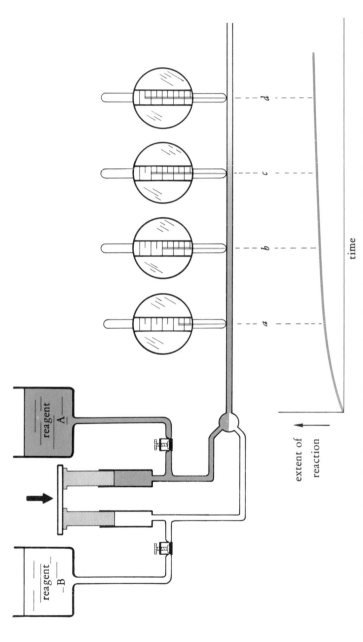

Figure 9–2. The extent of reaction in a rapid-flow experiment can be measured by the change in temperature. The temperatures at thermometers a, b, c, and d are different because the extent of reaction at each of these points is different and, therefore, the heat evolved is different at each point.

115

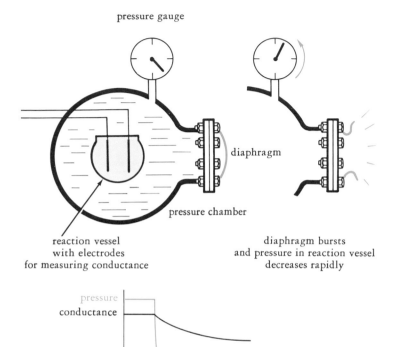

pressure gauge

diaphragm

pressure chamber

reaction vessel
with electrodes
for measuring conductance

diaphragm bursts
and pressure in reaction vessel
decreases rapidly

pressure
conductance

time

Figure 9–3. The pressure-jump method of displacing
an equilibrium very rapidly. For the reaction

$$Fe(OH_2)_6{}^{3+} + Cl^- = Fe(OH_2)_5Cl^{2+} + H_2O$$

the approach to the new equilibrium can be followed
by measurement of conductance. As shown in the graph
the conductance decreases because ion association occurs
to reestablish equilibrium at the lower pressure.

ture or pressure, is reached in a first-order change. The half-time
depends upon the equilibrium concentrations and the rate constants
in the mechanism. Although measurement of a high rate still depends upon some rapidly responding detection device, the problem
of mixing reactants rapidly has been avoided.

Formation of monochloroiron(III) ion in aqueous solution,

$$Fe(OH_2)_6{}^{3+} + Cl^- = Fe(OH_2)_5Cl^{2+} + H_2O,$$

is accompanied by a slight increase in volume. This change in volume per mole of product formed is much, much smaller than the change in volume accompanying gas-phase reactions in which the number of gas molecules changes with occurrence of reaction, e.g.,

$$2NH_3 = N_2 + 3H_2.$$

To shift equilibrium in the ionic reaction in solution, therefore, requires a relatively large change in pressure, 50 atm. For the reaction of hydrated iron(III) ion and chloride ion, the rate of reestablishment of equilibrium is measured by following the change in conductance of the solution by using a Wheatstone bridge with an oscilloscope to detect balance. Although this equilibrium is established quite rapidly, the rate is very much lower than the rate of diffusion of the ions together. This relative slowness can be attributed to the necessity of chloride ion actually displacing a water molecule bonded to iron(III), or, in the reverse reaction, the opposite change. Although iron(III) ion in aqueous solution is often represented simply as Fe^{3+}, this ion and other cations of multiple charge form discrete hydrated ions. Bonding in these hydrated ions involves partial donation of an electron pair on oxygen of the water molecule to the metal ion. It takes energy to break these bonds; the activation energy for formation of monochloroiron(III) ion is approximately 9 kcal/mole.

Before the advent of methods for studying very fast reactions, the rate of formation of many complex ions of iron(III) (e.g., with chloride ion and thiocyanate ion) could not be measured; they occurred too rapidly. On this basis, these iron(III) systems were considered labile and were contrasted with the corresponding inert chromium(III) systems. We now realize that, as striking as the contrast between iron(III) and chromium(III) systems is, the differences result from only approximately ten kilocalories in activation energy. In the case of formation of monothiocyanato complexes of these two metal ions, a factor of $\sim 10^8$ difference in rate at 300°K is the consequence of ~ 11 kcal of activation energy.[1]

---

[1] By use of the Arrhenius equation, the reader should verify this.

An equilibrium playing a central role in reactions relating to acidity and basicity of aqueous solutions is

$$2H_2O \underset{k_r}{\overset{k_f}{\rightleftharpoons}} H_3O^+ + OH^-.$$

Although this equilibrium is established very rapidly, the second-order rate constant for combination of hydronium ion and hydroxide ion has been obtained by using a relaxation method somewhat more elaborate than those already discussed. At 25°C this second-order rate constant is $k_r = 1.4 \times 10^{11}$ liter/mole/sec, the largest second-order rate constant known for a reaction in solution. To indicate the meaning of a second-order rate constant of this magnitude, it can be calculated that 0.10 M solutions of strong acid and strong base, *if mixed instantaneously*, would be half-reacted in $\sim 10^{-8}$ sec and 99 per cent reacted in $\sim 10^{-6}$ sec.

The equilibrium constant for the dissociation of water written in the conventional way is

$$K = [H_3O^+][OH^-] = 1.0 \times 10^{-14}\ \text{mole}^2/\text{liter}^2$$

at 25°C. Just as the concentration of solvent water does not appear in a conventional equilibrium constant because that concentration is is essentially the same in all dilute solutions, the concentration of water does not appear in the rate law, which is

$$\frac{d[H_3O^+]}{dt} = k_f - k_r[H_3O^+][OH^-].$$

This rate law involves a zero-order rate constant k_f, which is the rate of dissociation of water in the absence of back reaction. The ratio k_f/k_r is equal to the equilibrium constant

$$\frac{k_f}{k_r} = K = 1.0 \times 10^{-14}\ \text{mole}^2/\text{liter}^2,$$

and the zero-order rate constant for dissociation of water has, therefore, the value

$$k_f = 1.0 \times 10^{-14}\ \text{mole}^2/\text{liter}^2 \times 1.4 \times 10^{11}\ \text{liter/mole/sec}$$

$$= 1.4 \times 10^{-3}\ \text{mole/liter/sec}.$$

This is not a very high rate of dissociation. If to water there were added some reagent that reacted rapidly with either hydronium ion or hydroxide ion but did not react directly with water, the rate at which the over-all reaction occurred could not exceed this low value of the rate of dissociation of water.

Rate constants for the second-order reaction of hydronium ion and other bases, e.g., acetate ion, and for the second-order reaction of hydroxide ion with other acids, e.g., ammonium ion, have also been measured by relaxation methods. It is generally found that values of second-order rate constants for these association reactions are only slightly smaller than the value for the reaction of hydronium ion and hydroxide ion. The large range of acid dissociation constants of known acids would appear, therefore, to reflect a large range of dissociation rates, since on the basis of these observations the combination of hydronium ion and various bases is essentially diffusion-controlled and does not vary with the strength of the base.

With development of relaxation methods to such a point that they are capable of measuring rates of diffusion-controlled reactions, it is no longer appropriate to say that any reaction occurs at an immeasurably high rate. It is clear from studies already made that relaxation methods are going to clarify problems in many areas of chemistry. This does not mean to say, however, that all problems in kinetics of very fast reactions are going to be solved in the next few years.

9–3. FLASH PHOTOLYSIS

If iodine vapor is illuminated with light of appropriate wavelength, the dissociation reaction

$$I_2 + h\nu \rightarrow 2I$$

occurs. The absorbed photon is represented by $h\nu$, where h is Planck's constant, 6.625×10^{-27} erg-sec, and ν is the frequency of the light in seconds^{-1}. Rapid recombination of iodine atoms occurs in a nonphotochemical reaction

$$2I = I_2.$$

This reaction consumes the iodine atoms produced by the photochemical dissociation reaction. Under steady illumination with

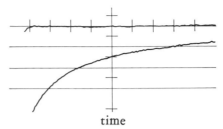

time

Figure 9–4. Oscilloscope trace showing scattered light
from the flash and the increase of molecular iodine concentration following its dissociation by flash photolysis.
The time lapse in entire period shown in this figure is
~0.003 sec. [From the work of R. L. Strong, J. C. W.
Chien, P. E. Graf, and J. E. Willard, *J. Chem. Phys.*, 26,
1287 (1957).]

light of moderate intensity, a steady state is established with only a
very small fraction of iodine dissociated to atoms. This steady state
results from equality of rates of photochemical dissociation of iodine
molecules and nonphotochemical recombination of iodine atoms.

If illumination occurs as a very brief and very intense flash, an
appreciable number of iodine atoms can be produced, and their recombination can be directly observed after the flash, Fig 1–1. In
actual experiments, the peak intensity of a flash may build up in 10^{-5}
sec and then decay over a period of 4×10^{-4} sec or less. After light
intensity from the flash has decayed, light of low intensity can be
used in a spectrophotometric arrangement to follow the increase in
concentration of molecular iodine. Figure 9–4 is an oscilloscope
trace showing the increase of concentration of molecular iodine following the flash in an experiment of this type.

This procedure, called flash photolysis, has contributed valuable
information regarding rates of very fast reactions such as recombination of iodine atoms. The technique has been used for study of reactions in solution as well as those in the gas-phase.

PROBLEMS

1. Slow reactions in solution generally are not made slower by addition of an inert substance which increases the viscosity of the solution. The rates of very fast reactions, on the other hand, are lowered by increased viscosity of the solution. Explain this.

2. The photochemical dissociation of iodine molecules has been discussed in this chapter. In an earlier chapter, we learned that the bond energy of iodine is 36 kcal/mole. What is the longest wavelength of light capable of dissociating an iodine molecule? (1 erg/molecule is equivalent to 1.44×10^{16} cal/mole; the speed of light is 3.00×10^{10} cm/sec.) (*Ans.: 7.95 $\times$ 10^{−5} cm*)

X

Isotopes in the Study of Kinetics and Mechanisms of Reactions

Isotopes can be used in a number of ways in kinetic studies and in other studies designed to elucidate reaction mechanisms. The use of isotopes as tracers allows one to answer many questions which would otherwise be unanswerable. In using isotopes as tracers, one generally assumes the chemical and physical properties of an element are independent of the isotopic mass. This is a good assumption for mass numbers greater than 20 to 30, but it is not a good assumption for lighter elements. This, however, does not preclude use of isotopes of lighter elements as tracers; it simply means that caution is required in interpreting results of certain types of experiments. The kinetic isotope effect can actually be turned to our advantage in investigating some questions regarding reaction mechanism.

The use of radioactive isotopes may simplify an analytical problem in a kinetic study. The decarboxylation of the amino acid alanine

$$CH_3CH(NH_2)CO_2H = CH_3CH_2NH_2 + CO_2$$

goes very, very slowly in aqueous solution. If, however, alanine labeled with carbon-14 is kept in solution for periods of a thousand hours, the very small amount of carbon dioxide produced can be determined by sweeping ordinary unlabeled carbon dioxide through the solution. It will sweep with it the very small amount of carbon dioxide labeled with carbon-14. This very small amount of carbon-14 can be accurately determined by counting methods. From such measurements, half-times of 4000 years or longer have been established for this reaction under various experimental conditions.

10–1. TRACER EXPERIMENTS

An obvious application of "tagged atoms" is the study of exchange of atoms between two different species. Without tagged atoms this sort of problem could not be solved.

Consider a perchloric acid solution containing iron(III) perchlorate and iron(II) perchlorate. No net chemical change occurs in this solution containing hydrated iron(III) ion and hydrated iron(II) ion. The frequency with which iron atoms change oxidation state is not measurable if both oxidation states are ordinary iron (a mixture of stable isotopes of mass numbers 54, 56, 57, and 58), but the frequency can be measured if one oxidation state is tagged with a radioactive isotope of iron. Iron-55, a positron emitter of 4 years half-life, has been used in experiments to establish the rate of exchange. If the radioactive isotope is present initially in the form of iron(II) ion, exchange will eventually distribute tagged atoms randomly between iron(II) and iron(III). Analysis of separated[1] iron(II) and iron(III) for their radioactivity as a function of time provides the rate of exchange. Studies at various concentrations of iron salts and at high acidity indicate one term of the rate law to be

$$\text{rate of exchange} = k_1[\text{Fe}^{2+}][\text{Fe}^{3+}]$$

with $k_1 = 0.87$ liter/mole/sec at 0°C. The magnitude of this rate constant corresponds to a half-time for exchange of $\sim$400 sec at 10^{-3} M iron(II) and 10^{-3} M iron(III). The activation energy as-

---

[1] The separation of iron(II) ion and iron(III) ion without causing additional exchange was a stumbling block to successful solution of this problem. The method finally used involved rapid formation of a complex ion of iron(II) ion and α, α'-bipyridyl, in the presence of which iron(III) can be precipitated as iron(III) hydroxide without coprecipitation of iron(II) hydroxide.

sociated with this pathway having an activated complex of composition $\{Fe_2(H_2O)_n{}^{5+}\}^{\ddagger}$ is 9.9 kcal/mole.

When tagged atoms of iron are randomly distributed between the two oxidation states of iron, no further net transfer of tagged atoms occurs. The exchange reaction elucidated by use of radioactive iron atoms occurs nonetheless in the absence of tagged atoms. Tagged atoms simply make the process observable. Analogous exchange reactions of different oxidation states of many metal ions have been studied by use of radioactive tracers.

The half-lives of radioactive isotopes of oxygen (oxygen-14, 76.5 sec; oxygen-15, 126 sec; and oxygen-19, 29.4 sec) are all so short they cannot be used in tracer experiments. Stable oxygen-18 can, however, be used as a tracer if the experimental results are analyzed with a mass spectrometer instead of the counting equipment needed in experiments with radioactive isotopes. One can purchase various compounds enriched in oxygen-18. Water enriched to 97 per cent with respect to oxygen-18 can be obtained. The sensitivity of mass spectrophotometric analysis makes possible good experiments with material that is much less enriched than this.

The exchange of water molecules between solvent water and the hydration shell of chromium(III) ion,

$$Cr(OH_2)_6{}^{3+} + H_2\overset{*}{O} = (H_2\overset{*}{O})Cr(OH_2)_5{}^{3+} + H_2O,$$

has been studied by using oxygen-18. At 27.5°C, the half-time for this exchange is 57 hr. It is the slowness of this exchange which allows unequivocal establishment of six as the number of water molecules bonded to chromium(III) ion in aqueous solution. Most other hydrated metal ions exchange their coordinated water molecules with solvent very much more rapidly. Special techniques involving the phenomenon of nuclear magnetic resonance have, for instance, established the half-time for exchange of water between hydrated manganese(II) ion and solvent to be $\sim 3 \times 10^{-8}$ sec. The factor of $\sim 10^{13}$ between these two rates arises from the difference of activation energies of the two reactions, 27.6 kcal/mole for chromium(III) and 8.7 kcal/mole for manganese(II).

Oxygen-18–labeled compounds can be used to settle other questions. An ester is formed by reaction of an acid and an alcohol.

Methyl benzoate is the product if benzoic acid and methyl alcohol react:

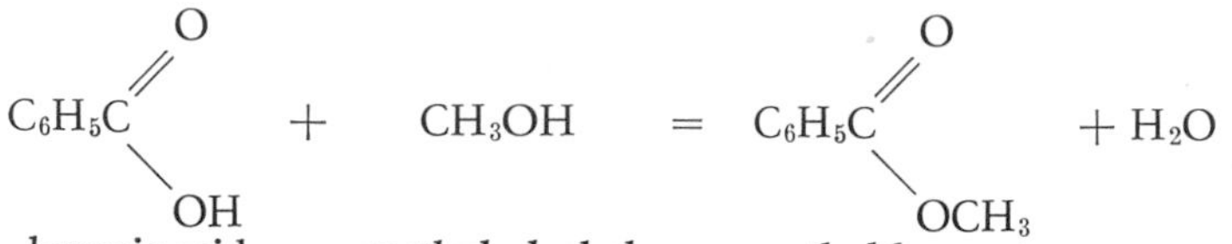

$$C_6H_5C\overset{O}{\underset{OH}{\big<}} \quad + \quad CH_3OH \quad = \quad C_6H_5C\overset{O}{\underset{OCH_3}{\big<}} \quad + H_2O$$

benzoic acid   methyl alcohol   methyl benzoate

Experiments with oxygen-18–labeled methyl alcohol have shown that the carbon-oxygen bond in methanol remains intact when methyl benzoate forms. The hydroxyl group which becomes water comes from the acid, not the alcohol (Fig. 10–1). Organic chemists predicted this result from the observation that the analogous reaction of benzoic acid and methyl mercaptan (a sulfur analogue of an alcohol) produced a thioester and not an ordinary ester.

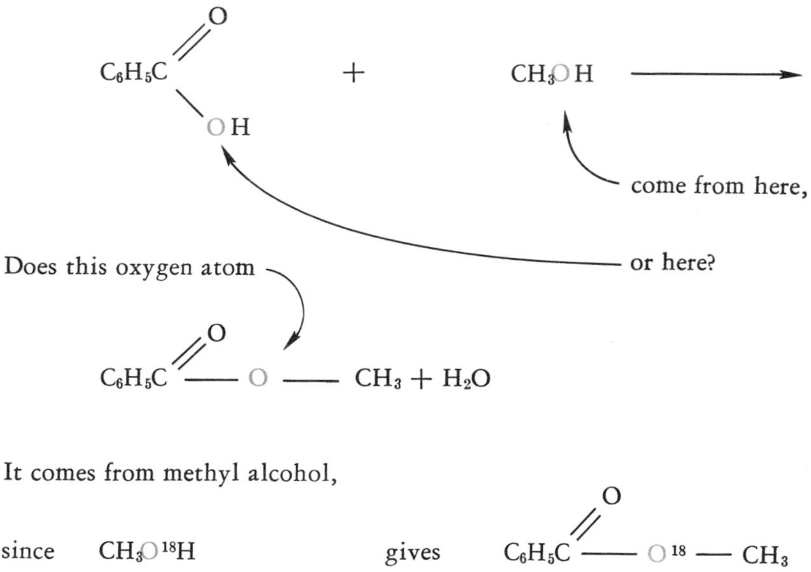

$$C_6H_5C\overset{O}{\underset{OH}{\big<}} \quad + \quad CH_3OH \quad \longrightarrow$$

come from here,

or here?

Does this oxygen atom

$$C_6H_5C\overset{O}{\big<} - O - CH_3 + H_2O$$

It comes from methyl alcohol,

since $\quad CH_3O^{18}H \quad$ gives $\quad C_6H_5C\overset{O}{\big<} - O^{18} - CH_3$

Figure 10–1. A question which was answered in a tracer experiment.

$$C_6H_5C\overset{\displaystyle O}{\underset{\displaystyle OH}{\big\langle}} \quad + \quad CH_3SH \quad = \quad C_6H_5C\overset{\displaystyle O}{\underset{\displaystyle SCH_3}{\big\langle}} \quad + H_2O$$

benzoic acid   **methyl mercaptan**   **S-methyl thiobenzoate**

10–2. KINETIC ISOTOPE EFFECTS

One can exploit the fact that reaction rates may depend upon isotopic mass to answer some questions about reaction mechanism. Kinetic isotope effects are essentially negligible for isotopes of mass number greater than 20 to 30, but they can be very large for isotopes of hydrogen. A big effect is expected if the rate-determining step involves breaking of a bond to hydrogen. To understand this, we must know something about zero-point energy, which can be introduced with reference to molecular hydrogen. The potential energy of two hydrogen atoms with electrons of opposite spin as a function of interatomic distance has been discussed at length in Chap. 5 and is shown graphically in Figs. 5–11 and 5–12. It is indicated at that point that not all possible vibrational energies are allowed. Vibrational energy is quantized; molecules can have only certain amounts of vibrational energy. In Fig. 10–2, the curve of Figs. 5–11 and 5–12 is repeated with allowed vibrational states shown as horizontal lines. Near the minimum the curve is essentially parabolic, with the consequence that molecular vibrations of small amplitude are simple harmonic in nature. The allowed vibrational energy levels are equally spaced with energies

$$E_v = (v + \tfrac{1}{2})h\nu_0 \qquad v = 0, 1, 2, \ldots ,$$

where v is the vibrational quantum number, h is Planck's constant and ν_0 is the fundamental vibrational frequency of the molecule. This fundamental frequency is a function of the mass of the bonded atoms

$$\nu_0 = \frac{1}{2\pi}\sqrt{\frac{k}{m}},$$

where k has a particular value depending on the nature of the bonded atoms and m is the mass of the bonded atoms. The minimum pos-

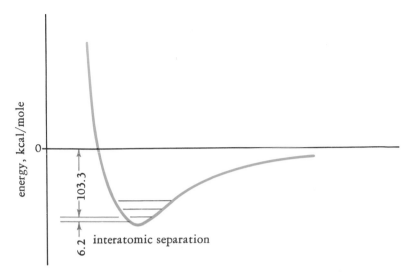

Figure 10–2. The potential energy of two hydrogen atoms with electrons of opposite spin, showing the lowest several vibrational energy levels. (The zero-point energy of H_2 is 6.2 kcal/mole.)

sible vibrational energy is, therefore, $\frac{1}{2}h\nu_0$. Even at absolute zero, molecules vibrate with this amount of vibrational energy. The potential-energy curves and values of k are identical for hydrogen and deuterium, but the value of ν_0 is $\sqrt{2}$-fold larger for hydrogen. The potential-energy curve for deuterium is given in Fig. 10–3. Because the spacing of vibrational energy levels is closer for deuterium than for hydrogen, and the lowest possible level is one-half quantum of vibrational energy above the minimum of the potential-energy curve, the energy required to dissociate deuterium is greater than that required to dissociate hydrogen. The dissociation energy of deuterium is 1.84 kcal/mole greater than that of hydrogen. This is not a trivial amount of energy. At 300°K this amount of energy corresponds to a factor of $\sim$21 in an equilibrium constant or a rate constant.

We would expect this difference in dissociation energy to be reflected in a greater activation energy for

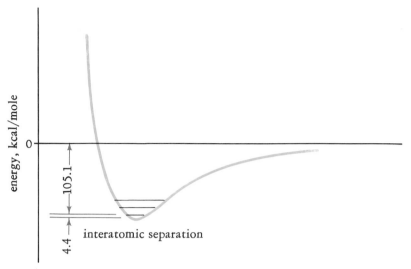

Figure 10–3. The potential energy of two deuterium atoms with electrons of opposite spin, showing the lowest several vibrational levels. (The zero-point energy of D_2 is 4.4 kcal/mole.)

$$Ar + D_2 \rightarrow Ar + D + D$$

than for

$$Ar + H_2 \rightarrow Ar + H + H.$$

Although these reactions have not been the subject of direct study, the effect being discussed has been observed in more complicated reactions.

In complex molecules there is a zero-point vibrational energy associated with each vibrational mode just as in the single vibrational mode of a diatomic molecule. The zero-point energy associated with a molecular vibration involving a bond to deuterium is smaller than that involving an analogous bond to hydrogen. If this bond is broken in the rate-determining step of a reaction, the deuterium compound is expected to react more slowly since the activation energy for its reaction will be higher than that for the analogous reaction of the hydrogen compounds.

A mechanism which was clarified by the observation of a large deuterium isotope effect is that for oxidation of isopropanol to acetone by chromium(VI) in acidic solution:

$$3(CH_3)_2CHOH + Cr_2O_7{}^{2-} + 8H^+ = 3(CH_3)_2CO + 2Cr^{3+} + 7H_2O.$$

Although transformation of

$$\underset{\overset{\displaystyle |}{H}}{\overset{\overset{\displaystyle OH}{|}}{H_3C-C-CH_3}} \qquad \text{into} \qquad H_3C-\overset{\overset{\displaystyle O}{||}}{C}-CH_3$$

definitely involves breaking the bond between hydrogen and the middle carbon atom, whether the breaking occurs in the rate-determining step or in some other stage of the reaction was not known until it was observed that isopropanol with deuterium substituted

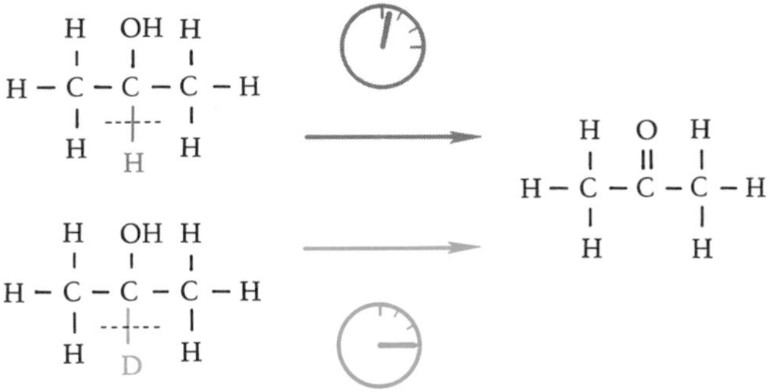

Figure 10–4. Kinetic isotope effect in oxidation of isopropanol by chromium(VI). The bond to hydrogen on the middle carbon atom must break in the rate-determining step, since the deuterium compound reacts 0.15 as rapidly as the hydrogen compound. [The rate-determining step also involves chromium(VI); this is not shown.]

for hydrogen at this position reacted only 0.15 times as rapidly as the compound containing ordinary hydrogen. Since the deuterium compound reacts sixfold more slowly than the hydrogen compound, the rate-determining step in this reaction must involve breaking the bond between hydrogen and the middle carbon atom, as illustrated in Fig. 10–4.

One unit of mass has a much smaller effect at higher mass numbers. Some molecules containing carbon-13 react 0.96 to 0.98 times as rapidly as the analogous molecules containing carbon-12. Measurable isotope rate effects have been observed even for sulfur-32 vs. sulfur-34.

PROBLEMS

1. The half-time for exchange of iron(II) and iron(III) by the pathway with an activated complex of composition $\{Fe_2(H_2O)_n{}^{5+}\}^{\ddagger}$ is 400 sec at 10^{-3} M iron(II) and 10^{-3} M iron(III) at 0°C. The activation energy is 9.9 kcal/mole. At what temperature is the half-time 1 sec at these same concentrations.

2. Two alternate possible mechanisms for the reaction of iodide ion and hypochlorite ion have been described in Chap. 6 and pictured in Fig. 6–1. Suggest a use of isotopic labeling that might indicate which of these two mechanisms is correct. Under what circumstances would your suggestion fail to clarify the situation?

Appendix

In this book chemical equations have been written involving each
of the signs

$$= , \quad \rightarrow , \quad \rightleftarrows , \quad \rightleftharpoons$$

There is a reason for using these several different signs. Some useful
information can be conveyed by the kind of sign used between the
reactants and products in a chemical equation.

The equality sign is used if only the stoichiometry of reaction is
given by the equation. The reaction may go in one step or by a pathway consisting of many steps; the reaction may be rapid or slow;
equilibrium may favor formation of products or may not. Regardless
of these features, an equality sign is appropriate in a chemical equation if only the stoichiometric relationships are of interest.

The single arrow $\rightarrow$ is used in an equation for either an elementary
reaction step occurring in one direction or for the sum of a sequence
of steps which is indistinguishable from an elementary reaction step.
Directly associated with an elementary reaction step

$$A + B \rightarrow C + D$$

131

is the rate law

$$-\frac{d[A]}{dt} = k[A][B].$$

Use of a single arrow does not mean the reverse reaction cannot occur; it means only that the reverse reaction need not be considered under the conditions in question.

The double arrow $\rightleftarrows$ has a significance analogous to that for the single arrow, except that both the forward and reverse reactions are taken into account. Directly associated with an elementary reaction step

$$A + B \rightleftarrows C + D$$

is the rate law

$$-\frac{d[A]}{dt} = k[A][B] - k'[C][D].$$

The special type of double arrow $\rightleftharpoons$ is used for equilibria which are established rapidly relative to the over-all reaction rates being considered. The reaction may or may not be an elementary one.

Glossary[1]

Activated complex: The configuration of atoms with the highest energy on a *reaction pathway*. Attainment of this configuration is the bottleneck of the *reaction pathway*. An activated complex is not like a normal molecule, even an unstable one; an activated complex is, by definition, in the act of flying apart to give the product(s) of the reaction step in question.

Activation energy: The energy of the activated complex relative to the average energy of the reactant molecules. It is defined by the Arrhenius equation

$$k = Ae^{-\Delta E_a/RT}.$$

The value of ΔE_a is obtained from the temperature dependence of the rate constant:

$$\Delta E_a = RT^2 \frac{d \ln k}{dT}.$$

Bond energy: The energy required to break the bond in question. Bond energies in the diatomic molecules hydrogen, hydrogen

---

[1] The terms are alphabetically arranged. If a definition involves another term in the glossary, that term is in italics.

iodide, and iodine are the values of ΔE for the gas-phase reactions

$$H_2 = 2H$$
$$HI = H + I$$
$$I_2 = 2I,$$

respectively. The C—H bond energy in methane (CH_4) is one-fourth of the value of ΔE for

$$CH_4(g) = C(g) + 4H(g),$$

since four equivalent C—H bonds are broken.

Cage, solvent: The envelope of solvent molecules surrounding one or more solute molecules. This concept has relevance in kinetics of reactions in solution, since reactant solute molecules trapped in the same cage make a large number of successive collisions and, therefore, have a good chance to react.

Catalyst: A substance or material which increases the rate of a chemical reaction but is not permanently consumed in the reaction. Substances which lower the rate of a reaction are called *inhibitors*.

Chain reaction mechanism: A mechanism which generates its own *catalyst*. The mechanism for a chain reaction consists of several steps, a set of two or more of which can repeat over and over again once they have been initiated. The chain mechanism given in Chap. 2 involves the following steps:

chain-initiating reaction

$$M + Br_2 \rightarrow Br + Br + M$$

chain-propagating sequence of reactions

$$Br + H_2 \rightarrow HBr + H$$

$$H + Br_2 \rightarrow HBr + Br$$

chain-breaking reaction

$$M + Br + Br \rightarrow Br_2 + M,$$

where M is the third body necessary both in the termolecular recombination of bromine atoms and in the bimolecular dissociation of bromine. In this mechanism, atomic bromine and atomic hydrogen are unstable intermediates which, because of their role in the chain-propagating reactions, are called chain carriers. These species are the intrinsic catalysts that the system generates.

Chemisorption: Strongly exothermic adsorption of gases by solids. Some type of strong chemical interaction must occur to account for the strongly exothermic nature of this type of adsorption. A contrasting type of adsorption of gases by solids accompanied by slight evolution of heat is called physical adsorption.

Diffusion-controlled reaction: A reaction with a high probability of occurring during an *encounter*. The rate of reaction under such circumstances is equal to the rate at which reactant molecules diffuse together.

Elementary reaction: A reaction that occurs in a single step. The reactants form the *activated complex* which gives the products. At most only a few chemical bonds are made and broken in an elementary reaction. Multistep reaction mechanisms consist of a sequence of elementary reactions.

Encounter: The event consisting of two or more solute molecules rattling around together in the same *solvent cage* for a while. Reaction may or may not occur in an encounter.

Enzyme: A protein which is a *catalyst* for a reaction in a living system.

Inhibitor: A substance which lowers the rate of a reaction. An inhibitor can act by converting a reactant or a *catalyst* to a less active species. (The term "inhibitor" is preferred to the term "negative catalyst.")

Intermediate, unstable: An unstable species produced in one step of a multistep reaction mechanism and consumed in a following step. It does not, therefore, appear as a reactant or product in the balanced equation for the reaction.

Isotope rate effect: The phenomenon of molecules containing isotopes of different mass reacting at different rates. For molecules containing isotopes of hydrogen of mass number 1 and 2, the isotope rate effect may be very large (a factor of up to 6 or higher) if a bond to hydrogen is broken in the *rate-determining step*.

Microscopic reversibility, principle of: The accessibility to the reverse reaction of each pathway for the forward reaction. A pathway for a forward reaction is also a pathway for the reverse reaction.

In a system at equilibrium, not only is the total rate of the forward reaction equal to the total rate of the reverse reaction, but
also the forward rate by each pathway is equal to the reverse
rate by the same pathway.

Molecularity of a reaction: The number of solute molecules or ions
coming together to give the *activated complex* in an *elementary
reaction.* Reaction molecularity and *reaction order* are not synonymous.

Order of a reaction: The sum of the exponents of concentration factors
in the experimental rate law. The *molecularity* of the rate-
determining step of an acceptable mechanism for a second-order
reaction need not be bimolecular. A mechanism consistent with
the second-order rate law

$$-\frac{d[A]}{dt} = k[A][B]$$

may involve two steps with a unimolecular *rate-determining step:*

$$A + B \rightleftharpoons Y \qquad \text{rapid}$$
$$Y \rightarrow P \qquad \text{slow,}$$

with the first equilibrium being unfavorable and the second
step being rate-determining. One can also speak of the order
of a reaction with respect to a particular species. The reaction
being considered is first order in A and first order in B.

Rate constant: A proportionality constant between the rate of reaction and the product of concentrations of species which influence the rate. For instance, k in the rate law

$$\frac{d[Br_2]}{dt} = k[Br^-][BrO_3^-][H^+]^2$$

is the rate constant for this rate law. The rate constant is also
called the specific reaction rate, since it is the rate of reaction
if the concentration of each species is unity, that is, one molar.

Rate-determining step: The first reaction step in a sequence of reaction
steps that has a gross forward rate equal to the net rate of the
reaction. It is the first reaction in the sequence the reverse of
which has a low rate compared to the net forward reaction rate.
Other reactions in the sequence are at equilibrium.

Reaction coordinate: A continuously varying parameter, each value of which corresponds to a set of coordinates of atoms of the reaction system along the *reaction pathway*. It is the energy of the highest energy point on the reaction coordinate which determines the reaction rate.

Reaction pathway: The sequence of the *elementary reactions* which comprise the reaction. Reaction pathway and reaction mechanism are synonymous.

Relaxation of a chemical system: The approach of a chemical system to equilibrium after being disturbed by a rapid change of temperature or pressure. The rate of relaxation is related to the rate of the chemical reaction.

Root-mean-square velocity: The square root of the average of the squares of the velocities of gaseous molecules. This quantity is derived from the kinetic molecular theory of gases.

Steady state: A situation in which the concentrations of reaction intermediates are approximately constant because the rate at which they are produced in one set of reactions is approximately equal to the rate at which they are consumed in a different set of reactions. Each of the latter reactions is not the reverse of one of the former reactions; if such were the case, the equality of rates being discussed would correspond to an equilibrium, not a steady state.

Steric factor: The reduction in rate due to special orientation necessary for colliding molecules if they are to react. A simple kinetic theory of the rate of bimolecular gas reactions leads to an equation

$$k = Ze^{-\Delta E_a/RT}$$

for the rate constant; in this equation Z is the collision frequency if each gas is present at 1 mole/liter and the factor $e^{-\Delta E_a/RT}$ gives the fraction of the collisions that have enough energy to be fruitful. The value of the *activation energy* can be obtained from the temperature dependence of k, and the value of Z can be calculated by using the kinetic molecular theory. With Z and ΔE_a known, one can calculate a value of k for a particular temperature and compare it with the experimentally observed value. For many reactions, values of the experi-

138 Glossary

mentally observed rate constant are smaller than the calculated values. This phenomenon can be accounted for in the equation by introducing a factor p:

$$k = pZe^{-\Delta E_a/RT}.$$

The factor p is called the steric factor, since it is assumed to measure the spatial requirements for a collision to be an effective collision. The steric factor may be very small if the reactive group of a molecule is only a small fraction of the "surface" of the molecule.

Transition state (see *Activated complex*): The "half-reacted" state in an elementary reaction. The terms "transition state" and "activated complex" are often used as though they are synonyms, although the former term really refers to the set of coordinates and the latter term to the group of atoms having this set of coordinates.

Zero-point energy: The minimum possible vibrational energy of the molecule. It is not zero; for even at a temperature of absolute zero, a molecule has vibrational energy. The zero-point energy for a particular molecule depends appreciably upon the mass of the vibrating atoms, being smaller the heavier the atoms. For isotopic substances, the difference between the energy of a molecule in the lowest vibrational level and the energy of the separated atoms is larger for the molecule with the heavier atoms. The activation energy for reaction of a molecule containing atoms of a heavier isotope is larger than that for the corresponding molecule containing a lighter isotope if the bond being broken in the rate-determining step of the reaction is one involving the atoms of greater mass.

Suggested Reading

Chapters dealing with chemical kinetics are found in all textbooks of physical chemistry. These include:

G. M. Barrow, *Physical Chemistry*, McGraw-Hill, New York, 1961
F. Daniels and R. A. Alberty, *Physical Chemistry*, Wiley, New York, 1961
W. H. Hamill and R. R. Williams, *Principles of Physical Chemistry*, Prentice-Hall, Englewood Cliffs, New Jersey, 1959
W. J. Moore, *Physical Chemistry*, Prentice-Hall, Englewood Cliffs, New Jersey, 1962

Books on Kinetics and Mechanisms

E. S. Amis, *Kinetics of Chemical Change in Solution*, Macmillan, New York, 1949
F. Basolo and R. G. Pearson, *Mechanisms of Inorganic Reactions*, Wiley, New York, 1958
R. P. Bell, *Acid-Base Catalysis*, Oxford University Press, Oxford, 1941
S. W. Benson, *Foundations of Chemical Kinetics*, McGraw-Hill, New York, 1960
F. S. Dainton, *Chain Reactions*, Wiley, New York, 1956
S. L. Friess, E. S. Lewis, and A. Weissberger (eds.), *Investigation of Rates and Mechanisms of Reactions* (Parts I and II), Interscience, New York, 1961 (I), 1963 (II)

A. A. Frost and R. G. Pearson, *Kinetics and Mechanisms*, 2nd ed., Wiley, New York, 1961

S. Glasstone, K. J. Laidler, and H. Eyring, *The Theory of Rate Processes*, McGraw-Hill, New York, 1941

K. J. Laidler, *Chemical Kinetics*, McGraw-Hill, New York, 1950

E. A. Moelwyn-Hughes, *The Kinetics of Reactions in Solution*, Oxford University Press, Oxford, 1947

G. Porter (ed.), *Progress in Reaction Kinetics*, Macmillan, New York, Vol. 1, 1961 (to be issued annually)

C. Walling, *Free Radicals in Solution*, Wiley, New York, 1957

Review Articles

B. J. Alder and T. E. Wainwright, "Molecular Motions," *Sci. Am.*, *201* (4) 113 (1959)

C. B. Amphlett, "Isotopic Exchange between Different Oxidation States in Aqueous Solution," *Quart. Rev.*, *8*, 219 (1954)

P. D. Bartlett, "Free Radicals," *Sci. Am.*, *189* (6) 74 (1953)

J. V. Becker, "Re-entry from Space," *Sci. Am.*, *204* (1) 49 (1961)

R. P. Bell, "The Rates of Simple Acid-Base Reactions," *Quart. Rev.*, *13*, 169 (1959)

J. D. Bernal, "The Structure of Liquids," *Sci. Am.*, *203* (2) 124 (1960)

G. C. Bond, "The Mechanism of Catalytic Hydrogenation and Related Reactions," *Quart. Rev.*, *8*, 279 (1954)

J. P. Chesick and A. Patterson, Jr., "Determination of Reaction Rates with an A. C. Conductivity Bridge," *J. Chem. Educ.*, 37, 242 (1960) (a student experiment)

F. R. Duke, "Oxidation Reduction Mechanisms," *J. Chem. Educ.*, 38, 161 (1961)

J. O. Edwards, "Rate Laws and Mechanisms of Oxyanion Reactions with Bases," *Chem. Revs.*, *50*, 455 (1952)

D. D. Eley, "Mechanisms of Hydrogen Catalysis," *Quart. Rev.*, 3, 209 (1949)

T. E. Ferington, "Kinetics of Polymer Formation by Free Radical Mechanism," *J. Chem. Educ.*, 36, 174 (1959)

E. Frieden, "The Enzyme-Substrate Complex," *Sci. Am.*, *201* (2) 119 (1959)

L. J. Grossweiner, "Flash Photolysis," *Sci. Am.*, 202 (5) 134 (1960)

J. Halpern, "Homogeneous Reactions of Molecular Hydrogen in Solution," *Quart. Rev.*, 10, 463 (1956)

J. Halpern, "Mechanisms of Electron Transfer and Related Processes in Solution," *Quart. Rev.*, 15, 207 (1961)

G. G. Hammes and L. E. Erickson, "Kinetic Studies of Systems at Equilibrium," *J. Chem. Educ.*, 35, 611 (1958)

C. M. Herzfeld and A. M. Bass, "Frozen Free Radicals," *Sci. Am.*, 196 (3) 90 (1957)

J. J. Katz, "The Biology of Heavy Water," *Sci. Am.*, 203 (1) 106 (1960)

J. W. Ladbury and C. F. Cullis, "Kinetics and Mechanism of Oxidation by Permanganate," *Chem. Revs.*, 58, 403 (1958)

L. P. Lessing, "High-speed Chemistry," *Sci. Am.*, 188 (5) 29 (1953)

G. Natta, "Precisely Constructed Polymers," *Sci. Am.*, 205 (2) 33 (1961); "How Giant Molecules are Made," *ibid.*, 197, (3) 98 (1957)

R. G. W. Norrish and B. A. Thrush, "Flash Photolysis and Kinetic Spectroscopy," *Quart. Rev.*, 10, 149 (1956)

J. D. Roberts, "Organic Chemical Reactions," *Sci. Am.*, 197 (5) 117 (1957)

D. A. Semenow and J. D. Roberts, "Use of Isotopes in Organic Chemistry," *J. Chem. Educ.*, 33, 2 (1956)

W. H. R. Shaw, "The Kinetics of Enzyme Catalyzed Reactions," *J. Chem. Educ.*, 34, 22 (1957)

D. R. Stranks and R. G. Wilkins, "Isotopic Tracer Investigations of Mechanism and Structure in Inorganic Chemistry," *Chem. Revs.*, 57, 743 (1957)

J. B. Sumner, "Enzymes, the Basis of Life," *J. Chem. Educ.*, 29, 114 (1952)

H. Taube, "Mechanisms of Redox Reactions in Simple Chemistry," *Advances in Inorganic Chemistry and Radiochemistry*, Vol. 1, Academic, New York, 1959, p. 1

H. Taube, "Rates and Mechanisms of Substitution in Inorganic Complexes in Solution," *Chem. Revs.*, 50, 69 (1952)

H. Taube, "The Role of Kinetics in Teaching of Inorganic Chemistry," *J. Chem. Educ.*, 36, 451 (1959)

C. F. H. Tipper, "Elementary Reactions in Gas-Phase Slow Combustion," *Quart. Rev.*, *11*, 313 (1957)

B. M. W. Trapnell, "Specificity in Catalysis by Metals," *Quart. Rev.*, *8*, 404 (1954)

W. A. Waters, "Mechanisms of Oxidation by Compounds of Chromium and Manganese," *Quart. Rev.*, *12*, 277 (1958)

Index